The Hundred-Mile-An-Hour Dog

Jeremy Strong once worked in a bakery, putting the jam into three thousand doughnuts every night. Now he puts the jam in stories instead, which he finds much more exciting. At the age of three, he fell out of a first-floor bedroom window and landed on his head. His mother says that this damaged him for the rest of his life and refuses to take any responsibility. He loves writing stories because he says it is 'the only time you alone have complete control and can make anything happen'. His ambition is to make you laugh (or at least snuffle).

Jeremy Strong lives next to a volcano in Somerset with his wife, Susan, and a flying cow.

www.jeremystrong.co.uk

D0415946

Jeremy Strong

The Hundred-Mile-
An-Hour Dog

Illustrated by Nick Sharratt

PUFFIN

PUFFIN BOOKS

Published by the Penguin Group
Penguin Books Ltd, 80 Strand, London WC2R 0RL, England
Penguin Group (USA), Inc., 375 Hudson Street, New York, New York 10014, USA
Penguin Books Australia Ltd, 250 Camberwell Road, Camberwell,
Victoria 3124, Australia
Penguin Books Canada Ltd, 10 Alcorn Avenue, Toronto, Ontario, Canada M4V 3B2
Penguin Books India (P) Ltd, 11 Community Centre, Panchsheel Park,
New Delhi – 110 017, India
Penguin Group (NZ), cnr Airborne and Rosedale Roads, Albany,
Auckland 1310, New Zealand
Penguin Books (South Africa) (Pty) Ltd, 24 Sturdee Avenue, Rosebank 2196,
South Africa

Penguin Books Ltd, Registered Offices: 80 Strand, London WC2R 0RL, England

www.penguin.com

First published by Viking 1996
Published in Puffin Books 1998
Published in this edition 2004

1

Set in 17/20 Bembo
Made and printed in England by Clays Ltd, St Ives plc

British Library Cataloguing in Publication Data
A CIP catalogue record for this book is available from the British Library

ISBN-13: 978-0-141-33270-3

*This story is dedicated to Molly and Mabel,
who between them taught Streaker everything she knows,
and a bit more besides.*

INTRODUCTION

BY JULIA ECCLESHARE, SERIES EDITOR

A dotty dog story, the brilliance of *The Hundred-Mile-an-Hour Dog* is that it is so gloriously ridiculous. Although it is firmly rooted in families, friends – and enemies – it effortlessly takes off into hilarious fantasy with the reader attached to the story as surely as Trevor is to Streaker.

Trevor knows that he's taking on an impossible job when he agrees to walk Streaker for the holidays. But a job's a job and the money is nice and, anyway, sometimes you just can't say no to Mum. He knows that he is on to a loser but there isn't much he can do about it. What happens next is as headlong as the title suggests, with more things going wrong for Trevor than even *he* had bargained for.

That's partly his own fault. Teaming up with his best friend, Tina, to help seems like a good idea, but making a bet with the odious Charlie Smugg is definitely NOT. And some of Trevor's ideas are completely barmy. What makes them funny is that he and Tina take them so seriously. Imagine thinking that you could communicate with a dog through a mobile phone strapped to your ear. Or that you could make a dog-walking machine by hitching a carpet belt to the back of an exercise bike. Crazy schemes, which get Trevor into one disastrous scrape after another.

Whether you're a dog lover or hater, it is impossible not to be completely absorbed into this story of a madcap but lovable dog and his equally lovable – and possibly almost as madcap – reluctant dog walker, Trevor (and, of course, his almost girlfriend, Tina . . .).

S treaker is a mixed-up kind of dog. You can see from her thin body and powerful legs that she's got a lot of greyhound blood in her, along with quite a bit of Ferrari and a large chunk of whirlwind.

Nobody in our family likes walking her and this is hardly surprising. Streaker can out-accelerate a torpedo. She can do 0 to 100 mph in the blink of an eye. She's usually vanished over the far horizon long before you have time to yell – 'Streaker!'

Dad refuses to walk her, point-blank. 'I've got backache,' is his usual excuse, though how this stops him from walking I really haven't a clue.

I tried something similar once myself. 'I've got front-ache,' I said. Mum gave me a chilly glare and handed me the dog-lead. She'll do anything to get out of walking Streaker too, and that is how the whole thing started. I ended up having the craziest Easter holiday you can imagine.

'Trevor ...' said Mum one morning at the beginning of the holiday, and she gave me one of her really big, innocent smiles. 'Trevor ...' (I should have guessed she was up to something); 'Trevor – I'll give you thirty pounds if you walk Streaker every day this holiday.'

Thirty pounds! As you can imagine, my eyes

boggled a bit. I just about had to shove them back in their sockets. I was so astonished I never twigged that what my mother was actually suggesting was MAJOR BRIBERY.

'It's the Easter holiday,' she continued, climbing on to her exercise-bike and pulling a pink sweat band round her forehead. 'You've nothing better to do.'

'Thirty pounds?' I repeated. 'Walk her

every day for two weeks?' Mum nodded and began to pedal. I sat down to have a think. Thirty pounds was a lot of money. I could do loads of things with that.

On the other hand – and this was the big crunch – I would have to walk Streaker.

Now, if someone came up to you in the street and said, 'Hey! What's the worst torture you can think of?', you might suggest boiling in oil, or having to watch golf on TV with your dad, or even the nine times table – which is one of my own personal nightmares. But without doubt I would have to say – walking Streaker. This was going to be a big decision for me.

I reckoned there had to be some way of controlling Streaker. After all, she was only a dog. Humans are cleverer than animals. Humans have bigger brains. Humans rule the animal kingdom.

I seem to remember that just as I was thinking this, Streaker came hurtling in from the kitchen and landed on my lap like a mini-meteorite. We both crashed to the floor, where she sat on my chest looking very pleased with herself.

Mum carried on quietly pedalling all this time. She must have known I'd give in. 'I'll do it,' I said. Mum gave a strange squeak and one of her feet slipped off a pedal. For some reason she looked even more pleased with herself than Streaker did.

'Can I have some money now?' I asked. (See? I'm not stupid.)

'Of course not.' (Mum's not stupid either.)

'How about half now and half when I finish?'

Mum free-wheeled. 'At the end of the holiday, when the job is finished, I'll give you the money.' So that was that. I had agreed to walk the dog every day for two weeks, and that turned out to be only one of my problems that Easter. I must have been totally mad.

TWO

I watched this film about a tank battle once. There were all these invincible armour-plated tanks. They were even bazooka-proof. The heroes were losing (of course), until Colonel Clever-Clogs (I forget his real name) came up with his BRILLIANT PLAN. 'We must use the tank's own strength against itself,' he said. 'If it's impossible for a shell to get through all that armour plate, it must be impossible for a shell to get out. We shall blow them up from the inside.'

And that's exactly what they did – brilliant film! Dad didn't like it of course. He doesn't like noisy action films with lots of explosions. He prefers watching golf, but have you *ever* seen an exciting golf match? I reckon golf would be a lot more fun if there were a couple of tanks playing and a few explosions. It would be quite interesting to see a nice big tank rumble across the green, square up on the tee, lift its powerful barrel and shoot golf balls right across the golf course.

So, what has all this got to do with Streaker? Well, I spent ages trying to work out the best way of dealing with the dog. I asked myself: what does Streaker do best?

PONG!

There were several answers to this:
1. Make a pig of herself.
2. Dig huge holes in the lawn.
3. Smell.

But I reckoned that the one thing she really shone at was speed. Streaker was a rocket on four legs. Maybe I could use her fantastic speed to my own ends. And that was when I remembered my roller-skates.

I hadn't used them for months. (I hadn't seen them for months.) All I had to do was hang on to Streaker's lead and that way she would get exercised and I'd get a free ride. You've got to admit it was a pretty jammy idea. Mum and Dad didn't think much of it though.

Mum sat at the lunch table in silence, eating her 99 per cent fat-free yoghurt that tasted like washing-up water. She obviously wasn't impressed. (She didn't think much of the yoghurt either.)

'I know your clever ideas, Trevor,' said Dad. 'They never work.'

'Yes they do,' I protested.

'Look what happened when you tried

to build an assault course in your bedroom.'

Parents have this amazing way of bringing your most spectacular failures into general conversation, don't they? I could feel myself turning bright red.

'That wasn't my fault. I didn't know that fixing a squiddly bit of rope to the ceiling would bring all the plaster down.' Dad grunted and Mum pushed the remains of her yoghurt across the table.

'Would you like to finish it for me?' she asked.

'Why do you keep trying to poison me?' I wanted to know. Mum gave me a wan smile and chewed the end of a celery stick.

I was determined to prove them wrong. I launched a major expeditionary search into the bowels of my wardrobe and eventually managed to find both roller-skates. I spun the wheels and they gave off a very satisfying *whsssssh*. How could this plan fail?

I kept Streaker tied to the gatepost while I put on my skates. Then I carefully unwound the lead from the gate, wrapped it round one wrist and crouched low behind her. 'OK, Streaker – lift-off!'

She hardly needed any encouragement. Her front paws churned away just like they do in cartoons and we were off, with Streaker's ears streaming out behind her like jet-trails. I was amazed by her strength and speed. Even pulling me didn't prevent her from quickly reaching something that felt like Mach one. Her legs pounded the pavement and she barked happily as we flew along. She loved it. I simply held on to the lead and felt the wind racing through my hair.

We skidded round the corner in great style and Streaker headed up the main road towards the street market. I reckoned it was time to slow down a bit, but of course I didn't have any brakes, and neither did the dog. Anyhow, by this time Streaker had switched to turbo-boost and there was no stopping her.

We hit the market at maximum speed, scattering shoppers in every direction. I held on for dear life as we zigzagged through the startled crowd, careering wildly from one side to the other. It was all I could do to stay upright.

Streaker suddenly swerved violently to one side to avoid a mesmerized old lady.

I had to fling out one arm as a counter-balance and somehow I managed to get her handbag stuck on it.

'Help! I've been robbed! Stop that boy! He's taken my bag!'

In no time at all the whole market seemed to be after me, but there was no way I could stop and explain. Streaker was really enjoying herself. There's nothing she likes more than a good chase. She doesn't even care if she's chasing or being chased. We went screaming round corners so fast that my skates started to smoke. We lurched into stalls, sending them tumbling over and spilling their contents every which way, crashed into people and bounced off them, and all the time the crowd behind was getting bigger and bigger and noisier and noisier.

'Stop that boy!'

'He's stolen an old bag's lady – I mean an old lady's bag!'

'Get the bag-snatcher!'

Streaker whizzed round the next corner so fast that she rolled over and over, and of course I just carried straight on and smashed headlong into a rack of dresses. Before I knew it I was hauled to my feet by a very angry mob. Not only was I still clutching the old lady's handbag, but I had a rather stunning flower-print sun-dress draped fetchingly over one shoulder.

To cut a long story short, I was carted off to the police station, along with Streaker. She sat attentively in the corner and looked completely innocent while I was almost arrested. Just to make matters worse, the policeman on desk-duty was Sergeant Smugg. He lives just up the road from us and he's got three Alsatians. (Personally speaking, I think half an Alsatian is a bit too much, but three!)

Sergeant Smugg rang home and Dad

had to come and get us. He wasn't very pleased, and not just because he had been dragged away from a nice kip on the sofa. Dad caught Sergeant Smugg cheating in a golf match last summer and they have been at war with each other ever since. I explained that it was all an accident. It was Streaker's fault.

Sergeant Smugg looked at the ceiling and rolled his eyes. 'Of course,' he said heavily. 'I should have known. The dog did it. The dog stole the handbag.'

'That isn't what I meant,' I said, and I tried to explain about the roller-skates and being towed and everything. Sergeant Smugg started laughing silently – you know, a sort of 'ha ha ha do you really expect me to believe that!' kind of laugh.

Dad was getting more and more annoyed at having his time wasted. 'It's quite obvious that Trevor is telling the truth, Mr Smugg,' he snapped. 'He's

hardly likely to make up such a story. It was the dog's fault. She's like it all the time.'

The policeman looked across at Streaker, who was still sitting there angelically. '*Sergeant* Smugg, if you don't mind, not Mister,' he insisted. 'And you can hardly blame the poor dog for all this.'

At that point the 'poor dog' suddenly came to life. Streaker leaped up, raced across the room, launched herself across the sergeant's desk (scattering everything on it to the four winds) and threw herself cheerfully into Dad's lap, despite the fact that he was standing up. They both fell in a heap on the floor and Streaker proceeded to give Dad's ears a good clean-out.

'What did she do that for?' demanded Sergeant Smugg.

'No idea at all,' Dad answered from floor-level. 'I told you – she's like this all the time.'

Sergeant Smugg frowned and shook his head. 'Your dog's loopy. She needs to see a dog-psychiatrist.' And he let us go home.

I won't bore you with all the things Dad said on the way back, but most of them carried threats of instant death. So, my first plan had proved spectacularly unsuccessful. Maybe it was time to call in reinforcements. I decided to go and see my best friend, Tina.

THREE

I know what you're thinking. HIS BEST FRIEND'S A GIRL! I've got used to the jokes. 'Trevor's got a girl-friend.' 'Trevor's in love.' 'When are you getting married, Trev?' I've heard them all.

It used to annoy me, but Dad pointed out that since it wasn't true it didn't matter, and that people only made fun of things when they were too stupid to understand – or just plain jealous.

Tina and I got to be friends when we first started school and discovered our birthdays were on the same day.

We even shared a birthday party once. Tina's taller than me. I'm a bit small and weedy, I suppose. My legs are really thin and bony. Sometimes I look at them in the bath and wonder how they manage to hold me up all day. Tina is taller and stockier. We had an Indian-wrestling competition once. I won't tell you who won. She's got loads of freckles, which she doesn't like. Don't ask me why.

Tina's got a dog too. He's called Mouse. This is meant to be a joke because Mouse is a St Bernard – you know, one of those dogs that looks like a Shetland pony that's run head first into a brick wall and got all its front squashed in.

Mouse is very well trained. When Tina says 'Sit!', he sits. When Tina says 'Fetch!', he sits. When Tina says 'Run!', he sits. In fact, if Tina shouted 'Ninety-nine per cent fat-free yoghurt', Mouse would sit. Compared to Streaker, he is super-intelligent. I thought Tina might be able to help, so I decided to take Streaker over to her place.

It took me a while to find Streaker. She was nesting under my duvet. She had stuffed the bottom of my bed with a jumper, two pairs of pants, a sock, a football boot, half a packet of crisps and an old apple core. Thank you, Streaker! I snapped the lead on to her collar and off we went.

You've never seen Streaker being walked, have you? It's not a walk at all. It's more like a series of gigantic jerks. We crashed into three lamp posts, visited four gardens that we weren't supposed to, almost tunnelled beneath a parked car in search of a very tasty week-old chip packet and finally used an astonished lady with a shopping bag on wheels as a kind of mini-roundabout.

When we got to Tina's house, she was

standing on the path holding the front door open. 'I knew it was you when I heard that lady scream,' she said. 'You'd better come inside and hide.' Streaker had already dragged me into the house. I think that Mouse is probably her best friend. (Funny how nobody makes jokes about *them* being in love.) I told Tina about the thirty pounds.

'That's brilliant!' she said. 'Why do you look so miserable about it?'

'Oh, come on, you know what Streaker is like!'

'Of course I know, but we can train her.

I helped my dad train Mouse and we don't have any trouble with him. I'm sure we can train Streaker, and then she won't be such a pain to take for a walk. It will be easy money! We'll start straight away. Let's go up to the field at the end of your road right now.'

I should point out that Tina is an ORGANIZER. (Mind you, you've probably worked that out for yourself already.) She likes deciding what to do and then doing it. What she likes even more is deciding what everyone else should do at the same time. She'll probably be a Business Manager when she grows up, or Prime Minister.

I don't mind being organized from time to time – it saves on having to make your own decisions – so we headed for the field. Mouse padded quietly beside Tina, while Streaker tried to wrench both arms from my sockets. It was quite a relief when we reached the field and I was able to let her off the lead.

WHOOOOOOOSSSSHHHH!! Was it a bird? Was it a plane? No, it was Streaker the Superdog, travelling at light-speed. All that was left was a cloud of dust as she vanished into the long grass. Every now and then her head bobbed above it and then she was off again. Mouse blundered amiably about the field like a furry bulldozer.

Tina and I wandered slowly round the edge of the field. There was no point in trying to follow Streaker: she was far too quick. Every so often she would burst out from the grass and go charging past, trying to knock us both over before diving back into the undergrowth. I tried to catch her a couple of times, but it was like holding out your hands and trying to grab a passing cannon-ball.

Tina yelled 'SIT!' as fiercely as she could whenever Streaker came hurtling past. Mouse would immediately plonk his big behind down, by which time Streaker had disappeared.

We stopped when we reached the old tin bath. At one time there were horses in the field and the bath was put there for them to drink from. It was three-quarters full of stagnant rain-water. I sat on the edge of the rusty bath and stared gloomily across the field. 'I've got to go through this every day for two weeks,' I muttered. 'I may as well give up now and drown myself.'

Tina picked up a stick and began to stir the black water. 'I wouldn't drown yourself in this. It's yukky.' A cluster of smelly bubbles burst on the top and several large water-snails slid beneath the scummy surface. 'Anyway, you give up so easily, Trevor. One minute you're full of bright ideas and the next you're going around like a wet weekend. I told you, we'll train Streaker.'

As if life wasn't bad enough already, it was at that moment Charlie Smugg popped up his big, fat face.

FOUR

You've guessed it. Charlie Smugg is Sergeant Smugg's son, and he's a real pain. I was always bumping into him, and his dad's three Alsatians – at least, Charlie was always bumping into me, deliberately. He's thirteen and enormous. He's got great gangly arms like King Kong, a face full of pimples and little piggy eyes. You know those pictures you see in books about Prehistoric Man? Well, he looks like that. Charlie likes pushing people around, as long as they're smaller than he is. Tina and I both come into the small category as far as Charlie is concerned.

'Well, if it isn't a pair of love-birds,' he began.

'You're right, it isn't,' Tina snapped back.

'Come out here for a smooch?' leered Charlie.

'Get lost!' she said. (I wouldn't have dared speak to Charlie like that!)

'What are you doing here, then?' he demanded.

Streaker made one of her rare guest appearances, flying past at Mach three, before doing a bombing run on a distant rabbit-hole. 'If you must know,' I said, desperate to prove that there was nothing going on between me and Tina, 'we're out here to train my dog.'

Did I tell you that when Charlie Smugg laughs he sounds like an asthmatic donkey? I thought he'd never stop. 'Train that dog?' he sniggered. 'You can't train a dog like that!'

'Yes we can,' insisted Tina. 'No problem.'

A sneering grin appeared on Charlie's

face. He reminded me strongly of Quasimodo, though I didn't tell him. And then he said the words that caused us so much trouble for the rest of the holiday.

'I bet you can't.'

'Bet you we can!' shouted Tina.

There was a strange sinking sensation in my stomach, as if I could sense trouble ahead, but it was too late to do anything about it.

'Right – you're on.' Charlie looked very satisfied.

'So, what's the bet?' demanded Tina recklessly.

Charlie took Tina's stick and trailed it through the sludge at the bottom of the old tin bath. It came out trailing great globs of green–black, slimy weed. Several more bubbles floated up, burst and filled the air with their putrid stink. Charlie smiled. He towered over us with a murderous look in his eye and dangled

the dribbling stick in front of our faces. 'If you haven't got Streaker trained by the end of the holiday, you have to take a bath – right here!'

Tina and I were too stunned, too horrified, too appalled to answer. We simply gawked at Charlie in dismay. He was really enjoying himself of course, and he hadn't finished either.

'You've got to wash your hair in it too, *both* of you.'

I stared in disbelief at the yellow scum floating in the bath. I felt like being sick, but Tina snatched back her stick and waved it at Charlie. 'Don't forget bets work both ways,' she shouted. 'If we *do* train Streaker, you have to wash here yourself.'

Charlie shrugged. 'That's OK. You'll never train her. I can't wait!' He turned on his heel. 'You can have your smooch now,' he added and strode off, laughing noisily. In the far distance I could see a neat black head with flapping ears appear occasionally. Streaker was homing in on Charlie like a cruise missile.

I nudged Tina and pointed. 'Five, four, three, two, one . . .'

There was a very satisfying yell and Charlie suddenly disappeared from view. A few seconds later he struggled to his feet waving a fist. We were too far away to hear what he was saying. I shall leave it to your imagination.

Charlie went on his way and I breathed a long, long sigh. 'Come on, we'd better find Streaker and start training her immediately. You've got us into a real mess now.'

'Me! I like that! I offer to help and end up getting blamed for everything. We're in this together.' Tina suddenly gave a giggle and stirred the murky water. 'Thank goodness we're not in *this* together,' she pointed out.

'Ha ha.' How could she joke about it?

'It's not bath-time yet,' said Tina cheerfully. 'You give up so easily. We are going to train that dog, Trevor, get the thirty pounds *and* watch Charlie Smugg sit in this bath and wash his greasy hair. Come on.'

What could I do but follow?

FIVE

Tina seemed to think that dog-training was dead easy. 'It's the same for any animal,' she declared. 'Dad taught me this special technique. It's called Behaviour Modification ...'

I have to admit I was impressed. It sounded as if Tina knew what she was talking about. Mind you, Tina *always* sounded as if she knew what she was talking about. I should have been suspicious, but instead I listened to her and really thought success with Streaker was just around the corner.

It turned out that Tina's amazing dog-training technique involved using an entire packet of dog-biscuits to try and bribe Streaker. By the time Tina had finished shouting and waving her arms about, there were no biscuits left and Streaker hadn't sat down once, or come to heel, or stayed anywhere. In fact, she hadn't done anything except become so fat that her stomach was now the size of a hot-air balloon.

Mum wasn't too pleased either when she discovered that a full packet of dog-biscuits had been scoffed in one afternoon.

'That's five pounds you owe me, Trevor. I'll take it out of the money I'm supposed to pay you at the end of the holiday.'

This was brilliant progress. I scowled at Tina. 'Great – so much for Behaviour

37

Modification. It's the first day of training and I end up owing money.'

'You did ask for my help,' Tina pointed out. 'If you're so clever, you can work out a plan for yourself.' And she left in a huff.

I didn't see Tina for a couple of days after that, which was probably just as well. I was a bit fed up about the dog-biscuits. Anyhow, most of my time was taken up with walking the dog. Some of you may be wondering why I didn't just keep Streaker on a lead the whole time. Well, if you've got only half a brain you'll have realized that if I had kept Streaker on a lead, then one of two things would have happened.

Either both my arms would have been stretched until they were about half a mile long, or I wouldn't have any arms at all because they would have both been pulled out of their sockets. Streaker would be rushing around wildly, trailing a dog-

lead with two arms clattering about on the end, all by themselves. Not very nice, eh?

The one good thing about spending hours waiting for Streaker to come back to me was that it gave me time to think. I decided that one of the reasons why Streaker didn't come when she was called was quite simply because she couldn't hear me. She was too far away. It was like trying to tell someone in Tibet that their breakfast was going cold.

I began to wonder how you *could* contact someone in Tibet. You could phone them, if they had a phone. You could fax them, if they had a fax. And then: KAPOWW!! This brilliant idea burst inside my head like a hundred firework displays all going off at once. Dad had two mobile phones at home, and a fax machine.

Of course, I could hardly send Streaker a fax, although the idea did give me a bit of a laugh. I could just picture Streaker rushing away with a fax machine tied to her back. All of a sudden there would be a loud 'beep-beep-beep-beep' and this message would roll out of the machine and dangle in front of her nose:

STREAKER – COME HOME AT
ONCE. LOVE, TREV.

No, the fax machine would be a bit
daft, but what about the mobile phones?
The more I thought about it, the better it
got, and I set about some careful
planning.

I waited until Dad and Mum went off
shopping, then seized my chance. I
nabbed both the mobiles, stuffed them
into a rucksack, grabbed Streaker and
headed for Tina's. Tina had an old pair of
binoculars that I reckoned would be very
useful. Streaker managed to avoid the
three lamp posts this time, but for some
strange reason she tried to mail herself in
a post-box. She kept leaping up and
jabbing her nose into the opening.

Tina wanted to know what the Big
Plan was, but for once I was doing the
organizing. We reached the field.

'Now what?' asked Tina.

'I'm going to let Streaker go. When I need to know where she is, I'll climb a tree and find her with the binoculars.' I grinned at Tina. Any moment now and my Big Plan would be revealed.

'Oh yes? And what do you do then?'

I opened the rucksack. Tina stared at the phones and wrinkled up her nose so that all the freckles got squashed up together. 'What are those for?'

'I'm going to switch this one on and

strap it to Streaker's collar. I'll use the other one to send her commands, and also I shall be able to hear where she is.'

'How?' asked Tina. 'What's Streaker going to do? Report back to you? I suppose she's going to ring you and say … "Woof woof, hello Trevor. I'm down a rabbit–hole by the railway line, back in two minutes, woof woof."'

'You're jealous,' I snapped angrily. 'Just because you didn't think of it. You're supposed to be impressed.'

'I am,' Tina went on, with a huge grin. '"Woof woof – Streaker reporting. Flying at thirty thousand feet and going in for my bombing run now."'

I had to laugh. You can never be cross with Tina for long. We strapped one of the phones to Streaker's collar, making sure that it was near one ear, and then we let her go. She seemed to think it was all great fun.

Tina and I climbed up a tree to get a good view of the whole field and keep track of Streaker. The binoculars were excellent. We didn't see much of Streaker but we got brilliant views of everything else. Tina turned them on to the rows of houses at the edge of the field. 'I can see your house and garden,' she said, steadying the binoculars on a branch. 'Your mum's put the washing out to dry. I can see your underpants!'

'Don't get too excited or you'll fall out of the tree,' I warned.

Tina swung the binoculars back over the field. 'I still can't see Streaker,' she said. 'Hey! There's Charlie Smugg, walking across the field. What's he doing?'

I snatched the binoculars from her and focused them on Charlie. Tina was right. He was stumbling across the field, pushing, kicking and cursing an old shopping trolley, with his three dogs

jumping around him. There was some
kind of large plastic tub wobbling about
in the trolley, and Charlie kept glancing
round, as if he wanted to make sure that
he wasn't being watched. He never
thought to look up in the trees of course,
but what on earth was he up to?

SIX

'Maybe he's been shopping,' I said.

'Don't be stupid, Trev. He lives up your road. He's hardly likely to go shopping and then drag it all the way across the field.'

'Well, what do you think he's doing, then?' I asked.

Tina checked the direction in which Charlie was heading. Her voice took on an excited edge. 'He's going to the bath. He's heading straight for the tin bath. Look, he's stopped. What's he doing?'

Charlie leaned over the trolley, puffing slightly. Yanking it across the field must have been hard work. Now that he had stopped moving about, I could see that it wasn't a tub in the trolley, but a large bucket with a snap-on lid. Charlie had another good look round, pulled the lid off and carefully lifted out the bucket. He balanced it on the side of the bath.

Even Tina could see all this, but she couldn't tell what was in the bucket. 'What's he doing!' she repeated impatiently. Charlie made one last furtive search of the area and then slowly tipped the bucket forward over the water. Out slopped something very dark green, something glistening with slime, something that looked like the Killer Sludge from Planet Sqwirkkk.

'Why is Charlie holding his nose?' cried Tina, and I let her have the binoculars. She was in time to see the last dregs of muck from the bottom of the bucket being emptied into the rusty bath. 'I don't believe it!' she cried. 'The dirty, rotten cheat. He's putting even more revolting stuff in there! You know what this means, don't you?'

'Yes,' I said. 'We're going to get very, very dirty when we get in that bath.'

Tina wasn't listening. 'He can't do things like that. It's cheating. This means war!' I had to admire Tina. I mean, declaring war on Charlie Smugg was a bit like Iceland deciding to attack America.

'What shall we do first?' I asked. 'Send in our non-existent tanks or blast him to pieces with our non-existent missiles?'

Tina coloured slightly. 'Well, it's not

fair,' she grumbled, 'and if there is anything we can do about it, then we're going to do it.'

'OK,' I agreed. '*If* there *is* anything we can do about it – we'll do it.' And I kept my fingers crossed in the hope that we wouldn't have to do anything at all. Call me a coward, call me a wimp if you like, but having a fight with King Smuggy Kong was not my idea of a good time.

Charlie Smugg and his dastardly deed were suddenly forgotten when I caught sight of Streaker in the distance and remembered my Big Plan. It was time to put it into action, so I handed Tina the binoculars, grabbed the second mobile phone and switched it on. My right ear was instantly filled with a swishing, crackling noise, which was Streaker careering through the long grass.

'Calling Streaker, return to base. I repeat, return to base.'

Tina began to splutter. 'She's a dog, Trev
– not a fighter plane.'

'Want a bet? Come in, Streaker!'

'I can see her,' cried Tina, peering
through the binoculars. 'At the far end of
the trees. There!'

'WE'RE OVER HERE!' I shouted
into the phone. 'Come on, it's time to go
home. Return to base.'

'She's coming back!' said Tina excitedly.

My mobile was filled with the sound of pounding paws and grass and bushes banging against the dog and phone. 'Hang on!' Tina gave a dismayed cry. 'Charlie's Alsatians are after her! Now what do we do?'

Sure enough, the three Alsatians were hot on Streaker's tail. I scrambled down the tree at breakneck speed, somehow managing to fall the last bit and land in some nettles. I struggled painfully to my feet and B A M M! I was immediately knocked flying by Streaker as she went charging past, panting furiously and heading for the road. Covered in a second set of nettle stings, I dragged myself upright once again and B A M M! B A M M !! B A M M M !!!

The first Alsatian spun me round like an egg-whisk, the second knocked me straight back into the nettles and the third simply pounded across my chest as if

some kind of very useful bridge had
magically appeared in front of it. The
Alsatians carried on the chase, barking
away merrily and obviously thinking that
the whole business had been set up for
their entertainment. Meanwhile, I sat in
the only clump of nettles in the world
that needed a set of traffic lights.

Tina dragged me out and we hurried down the road, just in time to see Streaker go whizzing into somebody's front garden, closely followed by three slavering Alsatians. Poor Streaker was trapped.

SEVEN

By the time we reached the house Streaker was crouching down on the front doorstep. Charlie's Alsatians were inching towards her, cheerfully showing great ranks of glittering teeth. As far as I could see there was no escape.

At that moment a ginger cat sauntered round the side of the house.

Now, you know as well as I do that dogs chase cats, but this cat was different. It was a monster. It hardly even looked like a cat. It was more like a ginger panther. As soon as it saw the three Alsatians all its fur stood on end so that it looked like an inflatable ginger panther. Its claws stuck out. It began to screech like some nightmare creature from a horror film and hurled

itself at Charlie's dogs. In two seconds flat
the dogs had vanished, tails between their
legs.

Tina and I grinned at each other. Even
Streaker looked pleased – until the
nightmare turned on her. Before we
could do a thing the cat had flung itself at
Streaker. For a brief moment it looked as
if she was going to get shredded by the
Moggy-from-Hell. But Streaker had quite
a different idea up her sleeve. (Not that
dogs have sleeves, but I'm sure you know
what I mean. If Streaker *had* got a sleeve,

then that's where she would have kept her idea.)

Streaker turned and – this was quite astonishing really – made a single flying leap from the front doorstep and straight through an open window. The cat plunged after her and in no time at all a fight had broken out inside. I started praying silently: *please don't let anything happen to Dad's phone.* Tina peered desperately through the window while I banged on the front door.

'What's happening?' I shouted, still thumping away with my fists and getting no answer.

'I don't know. I saw something large fly through the air. It may have been the cat, but I think it was your dad's mobile phone being a bit too mobile.'

That was it. I had to do something. Pushing Tina away, I saw Streaker and the cat go skidding out of the room. I started

clambering through the window. 'I've got to get her.'

'Supposing somebody comes?' Tina asked anxiously.

'They're all out. I've got to get Dad's phone back before it's completely smashed.'

Tina only hesitated a fraction longer. 'I'm coming too,' she said and hopped in behind me.

There were quite a few tufts of fur lying around on the carpet, some black and some ginger. I found a bit of plastic and my heart dive-bombed into my boots and hid there squealing with terror.

'There's another bit over here,' Tina called out helpfully, picking up a large but useless lump of ex-mobile phone. 'At least it wasn't the cat,' she added.

To find Streaker all we had to do was follow the noise. The two animals seemed to have started Round Three upstairs. It was a bit spooky creeping around somebody else's house, but I hardly had time to think about it. This was an emergency. If Dad's phone was beyond repair, then I was going to end up a hospital case.

Tina and I had just reached the top landing when a door opened as if by magic and this woman appeared, wrapped in a towel, her face smeared all over with thick white paste and her head smothered in curlers. She looked so weird that I just stood there and screamed. So did she, and she could scream much louder than me. Even Streaker and the cat stopped to see what all the fuss was about.

The woman grabbed the first thing that came to hand, which happened to be a rather large and menacing laundry basket,

and came straight at us, yelling like a Red Indian on a scalping mission. I was terrified, and so was Tina. She yanked open the nearest door, dashed inside, pulled me into the room with her and slammed it shut behind us.

It took me one second to realize that Tina had made a BIG MISTAKE. We weren't in a room at all; we were locked in a broom cupboard. It was dark, the handle was on the outside of the door, and there was no way out. I sank to the floor and buried my head in my hands.

'Well done, Tina,' I murmured. 'Nice one.'

It seemed like ages before we were released. I heard voices outside and the door was opened. I stumbled out, eyes blinking against the bright daylight and walked straight into the outstretched arms of a policeman.

'Well, well, well,' smirked Sergeant

Smugg. (I used to think policemen only said 'well, well, well,' in bad films. Maybe this *was* a bad film – it certainly felt like it to me.) 'We've caught two petty criminals red-handed. Breaking and entering private property with intent to steal – that's a jail sentence of five years or so.'

'Listen,' I began, 'it's all a mistake. My dog came …'

'Your dog!' Sergeant Smugg roared

with laughter and turned to the lady. 'This is what he said last time. He always blames it on his dog.'

'There wasn't any dog,' said the woman. 'Just these two – on my landing.'

'But there *was*,' Tina insisted and she tried to explain. The sergeant wouldn't have any of it and we were carted off to the police station, where they made a great show of taking our fingerprints and all our details before they would telephone home.

Dad came to fetch us. He wasn't very pleased – in fact he was managing a pretty good imitation of an erupting volcano on two legs. This was because Streaker had finally returned home, with half a mobile phone still strapped to her collar.

The woman decided not to press charges against us after all, probably because she could see that having to go home with Dad was going to be a far

worse sentence than going to jail. I would have been a lot safer in jail, I reckon. The only good thing was that when Dad discovered the Smuggs' Alsatians had been involved, he had a real go at the sergeant. Dad didn't like the Smuggs' dogs any more than I did.

So, there you are. I had now ended up

at the police station twice in one week. I still had to walk Streaker and I now owed Dad billions of pounds for his broken mobile.

Isn't life wonderful?

EIGHT

Parents do go on sometimes, don't they? And on and ON and ON. I thought Dad would never let the subject drop. The first hour was the worst, of course. You know what it's like. We've all been there. I never can understand why people shout when they get angry.

What's the point? Usually they're standing as close to your ear-holes as they can possibly get, so why do they have to shout?

Dad had a good rant and rave. So did Mum. This bawling-out was delivered in full de-luxe stereo. There was nothing I could say in my defence. Well, what *could* I have said? I just let Mum and Dad get on with it and patiently waited until they had finished. Then they began shouting at me because they thought I wasn't listening. I ask you! Even the Eskimos in Greenland were getting fed-up with listening to them.

'Aren't you the least bit sorry?' Dad repeated again and again, and his face kept switching from red to purple to white and back to red again. Of course I was sorry! I'd said I was sorry about fifty times already, but apparently that wasn't enough. I wanted to say: 'Look, Dad, me saying sorry for the millionth time is not going to repair your mobile phone,' but I had a strong feeling that it probably wasn't a good idea.

'Well, you're going to have to pay for a replacement,' Dad growled vengefully.

Where do parents get these crazy ideas from? There was no way I had the money to pay for a mobile phone. If I walked Streaker until Christmas I still wouldn't have enough money. Secondly, all my pocket money comes from Mum and Dad in the first place. If you look at it logically, that meant that they would be buying the phone with their own money anyway! (Another strong feeling told me that it would *not* be a good idea to point this out to my parents.)

Luckily Mum asked Dad if the phone had been insured, and it had. That meant that all Dad had to do was ring the insurance company and tell them that

Streaker had run off with it or that some monster–moggy had eaten it, and they would pay for a replacement. Dad was quite pleased when he realized this. I'm sure he knew that there was no chance of me coming up with the money. On the other hand, he was still annoyed because he reckoned I was getting off lightly.

'How long were you trying out this totally stupid idea of yours?' he asked.

'About half an hour.'

'Half an hour!' (Another explosion from Dad. I was beginning to reckon that if there was some way of harnessing Dad to a power station, his explosions could be turned into enough electricity to light up half the country. Imagine it. People would be sitting at

home when the lights began to dim, and somebody would say, 'Hey! Lights are fading! Somebody go and poke Trevor's dad – that'll get them going again!')

'Half an hour!' repeated Dad. 'Do you know how much it costs for a half-hour call on a mobile?' This is another continual source of astonishment to me. I'm eleven: does Dad really think I know how much his phone calls cost?

To cut a long bawling-out short, Dad decided I must have run up a bill of at least five pounds, which I would have to repay. Dad seemed fairly satisfied now that he had delivered his punishment and I was left in peace. At last. So that was another five pounds gone. So far I had lost at least ten pounds, because of paying for the dog-biscuits and the phone bill, and I hadn't actually earned anything yet.

I decided to keep a low profile for a while. You know how it is when your parents get in one of their blame-you-for-everything moods. Mum ran out of yoghurt – that was my fault. Dad couldn't find his golfing cap – that was my fault too. The car wouldn't start – my fault again.

They kept glaring at me and muttering, 'What's that boy been up to now?'

I wanted to jump up and confess: 'Yes! It was me! I really don't know what made

me do it. I must have been born to be bad. I filled Dad's golfing cap with yoghurt and stuffed it in the car's petrol tank.'

Needless to say I kept quiet.

I didn't go and see Tina for a couple of days and walked Streaker by myself, which was a real chore. I was getting desperate. Over half the holiday had gone and I still hadn't trained Streaker.

Just to make matters worse, I discovered what Charlie Smugg had tipped into the tin bath – frog-spawn.

There were great dollops of translucent grey jelly slopping about on top of the scummy water. I stood and stared, imagining what it was going to be like climbing into that disgusting, clammy gunge. Charlie couldn't go around doing things like this! It was cheating. I'd have to tell Tina.

I bumped into Charlie on the way

there. Or rather, he bumped into me. 'Wotcha, lover-boy! Off to see your girl-friend?' (Charlie's got such a tremendous imagination – I don't think.)

I looked him straight in the eye. 'You've been up at the field.'

'Yeah?'

'You put frog-spawn in the bath.'

'I never! It must have been the frogs!'

'What frogs? The only frog I saw was pushing a shopping trolley across the field with a bucket of frog-spawn in it.'

Charlie was really startled at first. 'Where were you? I never saw you.' Then he grinned. 'So what if I did?' he said cockily. 'What are you going to do about it?'

He stepped closer and towered over me. (Have you ever noticed that when people are far away you can feel really brave about facing up to them? I reckon it's because when they're far away they look a lot smaller, so you're not so scared. Unfortunately, the closer they get, the bigger they get and, just at this precise moment, Charlie Smugg was looking very big indeed.)

'It's cheating,' I insisted, and all at once I saw a way out of the bet. 'You've cheated and that means the bet is off. We're not going to bathe in that old tin tub.'

Charlie folded his huge arms across his chest. 'I don't care,' he sneered. 'Because if you don't get in yourselves, I'll just pick you up and put you in myself. Got it?' He reached out, seized me by both arms, and lifted me six inches clear of the pavement. I could feel his fingers, like iron bands, squeezing round my puny arms. My heart was thundering away and I really thought I was going to become strawberry jam. Charlie shoved his fat, pimply face right up close to mine.

'See what I mean?' he grinned, and plonked me back down. He pushed past and went up the road, laughing.

I was not in a very good mood when I reached Tina's and by the time I had finished telling her about Charlie, she wasn't very happy either.

'Frog-spawn!'

'Yes – frog-spawn. There wasn't any frog-spawn in there before. It's bubbling over with the stuff now.'

Tina was seething. 'He can't do that!' she cried. 'It's against the Geneva Convention! We'll take him to the European Court of Human Rights!'

I nodded glumly. 'Yeah – he can't do things like that. Trouble is – he has.' After my most recent encounter with Charlie I knew for certain that there was absolutely no chance of escaping our fate, unless we wanted to become the latest batch of strawberry jam.

I didn't think life could get any worse. Streaker was uncontrollable and we were doomed to drown in frog-spawn.

'What also gets me,' I grumbled, 'is that everybody seems to think we're in love. They think you're my girlfriend!'

'You don't have to look so disgusted by the idea,' Tina pointed out.

'Well, you know what I mean. They're all stupid.'

'Yeah,' Tina said quietly. Her face had this strange look on it, as if she was smiling. But she wasn't – at least her mouth wasn't, if you see what I mean.

'Cheer up,' she said. 'You're such a pessimist. We haven't lost the bet yet and there's still some of that thirty pounds left. I've been thinking about Streaker and I've had an idea . . .'

What? Tina's the Organizer. *I'm* the Ideas Man. I glanced at her suspiciously. 'Yeah? What is it?'

Actually it *was* a good one. I had known all along that it was Streaker's speed that we had to do something about. The roller-skates would have been OK if it hadn't been for the fact that neither the skates nor the dog had any brakes. Tina's idea was to use our bikes, which at least *did* have brakes, and her skateboard.

'We can't tie Streaker to your skateboard,' I said. 'That won't exercise her.'

'I'm not going to tie Streaker to the board. I'm going to tie her bowl to the board and fill it up with food.' Tina had this big grin all over her freckled face. 'We tow the skateboard and Streaker gallops along behind.'

'Brilliant!' I agreed. 'As long as we keep away from the main roads. We could use the track that runs along the edge of the field. Let's do it!'

We paid a fleeting visit to my house to collect Streaker, her bowl, some food and my bike and went back to the field. I let Tina take control since this was her idea. Anyhow, I needed both arms to hang on to Streaker, who was tugging at her lead in her desperation to get at the dog food. Tina got some string, tied the bowl to her skateboard and filled it with meaty chunks. She fixed some rope between her bike and the skateboard.

'Wait until I'm a little way ahead and then let her go,' she ordered. Tina climbed on to her bike and set off. I waited a few seconds and then unclipped the dog-lead. Streaker was off like a starving Exocet missile. I leaped on my bike and set off after them.

It was working brilliantly! Tina raced ahead, with the skateboard skimming along behind her and Streaker just about keeping pace, but not quite able to reach her bowl. She had half a mile of tongue hanging out. I went whizzing after them, and round the track we hurtled.

'It's great!' I yelled. 'Keep going!'

The track ran parallel to the road for a short distance, with just a thin strip of tussocky grass between them. We were

charging along this bit at a fine speed
when a police car drew up alongside and
kept pace with us. Sergeant Smugg
wound down his window.

'Hey! What do you think you're up to?'
he bellowed, and the car's siren burst into
a high-pitched wail.

Tina almost jumped out of her skin and
swerved to one side. The skateboard
lurched violently in the same direction.
The dog bowl flew off, went sailing

through the air, straight through the car window and splatted wrong way up on top of Sergeant Smugg's head.

As if that wasn't bad enough, Streaker went pounding after it. She zoomed through the window and immediately set about eating the dog food, even though most of it was still stuck to the sergeant's head.

Unfortunately he was still trying to drive his car. He did manage to keep going a little further, even though

Streaker was bouncing up and down in his lap and taking great slurping licks at his face. Eventually a thick hedge and a deep ditch stopped any further progress. Clouds of steam belched out from a punctured radiator. The siren gave a last feeble wail of despair and died.

Sergeant Smugg struggled out, flailing his arms like a hyperactive windmill in a futile bid to keep Streaker at bay. I threw a glance at Tina and noted that she looked just like I felt – nerve-numbingly horrified. It was definitely going to be prison this time.

The end-result of all this was that Tina and I paid yet another visit to the police station, only we had to wait until a second police car came, and a breakdown truck too. Sergeant Smugg insisted on arresting Streaker, and the skateboard and the dog bowl. 'It's all evidence for the prosecution,' he scowled.

'You've got a meaty chunk stuck behind your ear, sarge,' one of the constables pointed out, winking at me. That made me feel a bit better: not a lot, of course, but it was as if someone was on my side.

Dad had to come and get us again. I thought he'd be furious with me, but in fact he aimed most of his anger straight at Sergeant Smugg, who stood there drying

his hair after having a shower and changing his clothes. Dad pointed out that:

1. He was getting fed up with collecting us from the police station and –

2. It was not against the law to tow a dog bowl behind a bicycle and –

3. It was all Mr Smugg's fault anyway – if he hadn't shouted and set off his siren Tina wouldn't have swerved.

'My name is *Sergeant* Smugg, not Mister!' roared the sergeant. 'Your dog has just wrecked my car! She tried to eat my head! If you can't keep her under control I shall order her to be destroyed.'

'You can't do that,' snapped Dad. 'If anyone ought to be put down, it's you!'

'Really?' bellowed Sergeant Smugg. 'I'm not the mad one around here. I reckon your dog's got rabies. She's totally crazy – and so is your family. Roller skates? Mobile phones? Skateboards and dog bowls? You're all loopy. One more episode like this – just one more – and I'll have your dog destroyed before you can say "Goodbye, Streaker." And you can thank your lucky stars that I don't have the rest of you put down with her. Now get her out of here!'

It was weird. Now that Streaker was under sentence of death everyone became very fond and protective of her. She had always been a pain, but she was also so bouncy and cheerful and, well ... mad, and we loved her for it really. We didn't want to lose her. Mum and Dad spoke to her nicely and her predicament united us as a family. We fumed about the unfairness of it all and I wondered if there was a European Court of Doggy Rights. Dad even gave her extra meals. It didn't change the way she behaved, of course. She was still pandemonium with four legs, a tail, and a woof attached.

We were all very worried about her. I was scared to take her outside. I thought that Sergeant Smugg, or Charlie, or their

Alsatians might pounce on us at any moment. Tina and I both felt pretty depressed. The holiday was almost over and it seemed inevitable that we would either get arrested or shoved in a bath full of frog-spawn and other assorted gunge. We couldn't win. However, Streaker had to go out sometimes and we went slinking up to the field in the evenings, hoping to avoid the Smuggs.

Then, two days before the end of the holiday, I discovered a ray of hope in the field. Actually, it wasn't exactly a ray of hope, it was a small heap of junk that somebody had dumped at the edge of the field. There was some old stair-carpet, bits of wood and some metal cylinders. I've no idea what the cylinders had been used for, but as soon as I saw them I got the most AMAZINGLY BRILLIANT idea ever. I grabbed Tina by the shoulders and stopped her.

'It's OK!' I shouted. 'We shall never have to walk Streaker again!'

'Has it got anything to do with mobile phones?' asked Tina. (She has so little faith in me.)

'No,' I said, seizing a couple of metal rollers. 'We're going to build a dog-exercising machine.'

'A what?'

'A dog-exercising machine, for exercising the dog.'

'Yes, I know what a dog-exercising machine is, Trevor. How do you plan to make one out of stair-carpet?'

'First of all, you have to say "You're clever, Trevor".'

'You're very clever, Trevor. You're the most clever Trevor ever.'

'I know. Listen, we put these metal rollers at each end of these wooden planks. The planks will hold the rollers in place. We loop the stair-carpet round the rollers. We make the stair-carpet move round and round. We put Streaker on the carpet and it makes her walk, *and we don't even have to leave the house.*'

I have to admit that there are times when I astonish myself. I'm not big-headed or anything (at least *I* don't think I am), but the more I considered this idea of mine the more I realized that it was mega-fantastic. Not only would Streaker get exercised, it would all take place indoors, where the Smuggs couldn't get her and where she was safe. There was no dog food involved, no mobile phones ... even my parents would be impressed – possibly – although I decided I wouldn't tell them right away.

(Have you ever noticed how your brain plays tricks on you? I mean, you'd think that by this time I would have known that *none* of our ideas had worked the way we had expected and we had spent most of our time at the local police station as a result.)

Tina didn't exactly look overwhelmed. There was obviously a snag as far as she was concerned. 'How do we make the carpet go round?' she asked. I grinned and felt all warm inside. This was the most mind-blowing bit of the entire plan.

'Easy. We use my mum's exercise-bike.'

'You what?'

'We use my mum's exer-cycle. All we have to do is connect the back wheel to one of the metal rollers, get on the bike and pedal.'

Tina whistled. I knew the idea would bowl her over. It was so beautifully simple.

'That's really clever, Trevor,' she admitted. 'Won't your mum mind?'

'She won't know. She's gone to aerobics. Then she does circuit training. She won't be back until the next millennium. Dad's up at the golf club. By the time they get back it will all be working like a dream.'

We collected all the bits we needed and hurried back to my house. Streaker carried the roll of stair-carpet in her mouth. If only she knew what we were going to do with it!

The first bit was easy. We fixed the

rollers at either end of the two wooden
planks. Putting the carpet round was a bit
more awkward. I cut it to the right length
and we both sat there and stitched the
two ends together to make a continuous
loop.

Connecting Mum's exer-cycle to one
of the rollers was not simple. We tried
using string, but that kept breaking. Then
I had an idea. (I told you I'm an Ideas

Man.) I had been in the car with Mum once when the fan-belt broke. Mum did this really clever thing. She took off her tights and used them to make a replacement fan-belt. It worked well enough to get us to the nearest garage.

Tina didn't think my mum would be too happy about me using her tights. 'She's got hundreds of pairs,' I said. 'She could put them on a giant centipede and still have lots left over. You hold this while I tie a knot.'

And that was that. We had finished. We stood back and admired our machine. It looked a little odd, what with Mum's tights driving the roller and a platform made from stair-carpet with lovely flowers printed all over it. Tina climbed on to the exer-cycle and began to pedal. The carpet started to roll.

'It works! Brilliant! It works! Quick, where's Streaker?'

The unsuspecting dog was fast asleep in an armchair. (That was pretty astonishing too. She must have worn herself out in the field.) I pounced on Streaker, carried her through to the dog-exercising machine and put her on the roller-track. She jumped off. I grabbed her and put her back on. She jumped off again.

'It's no good. She won't stay there. Look, you get the track rolling and I'll put her on when you've got some speed up. She'll soon get the idea.'

Tina began pedalling and shortly the rollers were whirling and the stair-carpet was clattering round and round. I hovered over the track, holding Streaker, waiting for the right moment.

'A bit faster!' I yelled.

Tina crouched over the handlebars and began to pedal as if she was in a Tour de France time-trial. The carpet became a brown blur as it trundled round faster and faster.

The moment had come.

ELEVEN

'Walkies!' I cried and dropp-
ed Streaker on to the
whirring track.

There was a startled yelp as Streaker was
caught by the carpet and hurled
backwards at high speed. She shot off the
rear of the track, whizzed out through the
door, rocketed across the kitchen, and
ended up with her backside rammed in
the open front of the washing-machine –
which luckily wasn't switched on.

Streaker fixed me with a bewildered gaze as if to say, 'How on earth did I get into *this* position?' Her front paws were firmly on the ground, but the back half of her was even more firmly wedged in the washing machine. I ran over and tried to pull her out as gently as I could, but Streaker was jammed there like King Arthur's sword in the stone.

'Now what?' Tina gave me a silent shrug.

'She can't move,' I went on. 'We've got to get her out. We need help.'

Tina shrugged again. 'What kind of help?' she said. 'Who do we ask? Plumbers? A garage? Fire brigade?'

'Fire brigade!' I leaped to the telephone. They get cats out of trees and things, don't they? Maybe they get dogs out of washing machines.'

It seemed the logical answer to me. The fire brigade could toddle around and they'd have Streaker out in a jiffy.

However, this was where we hit our next little problem. I wanted to ring the fire station and have a friendly chat about stuck dogs, but you can't ring the fire station without dialling 999. The telephone was answered immediately and I kept saying, 'Look, this isn't an emergency, but ...'

The next thing we heard was *DEEE-DOOOO DEEE-DOOOO DEEE-DOOOO!!* Talk about embarrassing! Two fire engines screeched to a halt outside and moments later the house was full of firemen racing around uncoiling hoses and dashing upstairs waving axes, ready to break down any doors.

'Where's the fire, lad?' asked the Chief Fire Officer.

'It's not exactly a fire,' I murmured. 'It's more like a dog stuck in a washing machine,' and I pointed out Streaker. The Chief Fire Officer was very good and he sized up the situation at once.

'Right, lads,' he bellowed, 'we need cutting-gear, and the pliers, and the grease – on the double. Got a bit of a doggy problem here. Take care – don't hurt her.'

Tina peeped through the front window. 'You've got lots of nosy neighbours, haven't you, Trevor?' It was true. The street was lined with about fifty people – all ages, all colours, all sizes, and all staring at us very hard and muttering among themselves.

In the middle of this Mum arrived home. Two fire engines were blocking the road in front of her home, with their orange and blue lights flashing furiously. Hoses dangled from every window and firemen were running in and out of her front door. She came rushing in, making even more noise than the fire sirens. 'Where's the fire? My house is going up in flames! Is everyone safe?'

The Chief Fire Officer tried to calm her and helped her to an armchair. 'Don't worry, madam, there's no fire, but your dog's stuck in your washing machine.'

'Streaker!' cried Mum, leaping up at once. 'She's being tumble-washed – she'll drown! Oh, the poor dog! Get her out!'

'It's all right,' explained the Chief Fire Officer, calming her again. 'She's going to

be fine. The machine isn't on. She just has a stuck bottom. It won't take long.'

At that moment one of the firemen shouted, 'She's out, Chief – no problem!' and Streaker went whizzing round everyone, barking with delight, jumping up and trying to lick their faces and generally looking remarkably cheerful and unhurt by her little adventure. The firemen all had a good laugh about it and Streaker probably got more pats than she'd had since she was born. Mum made them all a cup of tea. After that they climbed back into their glorious machines and tootled back to the station.

Mum waved them goodbye, all smiles, then came back inside and shut the front door with an ominous bang. She glared at her exer-cycle, her tights and the old stair-carpet. I could tell she knew there must be a connection between this weird contraption in the front room and Streaker getting jammed in the washing machine.

'Right, then,' she hissed. 'Let's hear it, Trevor, and it had better be good.' My heart sank, rather like the *Titanic,* only a lot faster and with no survivors.

'It was my idea, Mrs Larkey,' said Tina, looking Mum straight in the eyes.

'Really?' Mum sounded as surprised as I was. What was Tina up to? I knew better than to own up at this point. It was best to let Tina get on with it.

'I suggested we build a dog-exercising machine.'

Mum glared at the stair-carpet. 'A dog-exercising machine?' she repeated. 'Using my best tights, I see?'

Tina nodded. 'I pedalled a bit too fast and Streaker fell off and got stuck.'

'We couldn't get her out,' I butted in. 'We were worried about her, so we ...'

'Called the fire brigade.' Mum finished off for us. For several moments she just stared at the contraption we had built. She took a deep, deep breath and sighed. 'I think you have both been very silly. Still, at least it wasn't the police this time. Now, clear up and get my exer-cycle put back the right way. You owe me for a pair of tights, Trevor Larkey.' She went huffing off upstairs to get changed.

I looked at Tina with relief. 'Phew! That was close. Why did you tell her it was your idea?'

She gave a little shrug. 'How many friends have you got?' she asked. I was a bit taken aback.

'Friends? I don't know. I've never counted. Not all that many I suppose.'

'How many?' she insisted. I thought for a few moments.

'I know quite a few people,' I stalled. I didn't want to say any more. It was too embarrassing.

Tina folded her arms. I could feel her eyes drilling into me. 'I don't mean people you *know*. They don't count. How many *friends*?'

'Boys or girls?' I asked, still stalling as much as possible.

'Either – both,' Tina answered nonchalantly. My face was burning. It must have been bright red.

'One,' I admitted.

'Me?' asked Tina.

'Of course,' I snapped. She gave me a quick sideways glance.

'That's all right then,' she said quietly. What was all right? What was she going on about?

'Anyhow, parents are never nearly so cross with other people's children,' she continued matter-of-factly. 'It's something I've noticed. Your mum would have gone on shouting for ages if she thought it was your idea. As soon as I said it was mine, she calmed down and went away.'

I sat there, stunned. Why had I never

noticed things like that? I think it's because Tina's a girl. Girls notice things like that. (Well, that's what I think anyway, and it's the only explanation *I* can think of.) Mind you, I was just about to be more stunned than at any time in my life, before or since.

TWELVE

'We'd better take the dog out,' Tina reminded me. 'She hasn't actually had any exercise yet.' I fetched the dog-lead.

'Come on, Streaker – time for walkies.' Streaker leaped to her feet, trotted straight over, plonked her bottom on the floor and waited for me to clip the lead to her collar. Were we astonished? No, that's

not the word – flabbergasted. That sounds better. We were flabbergasted. Streaker looked up at me with eyes that seemed to say 'All right, I'll do *anything*, but don't jam my bum in the washing machine again!'

'Pinch me, I'm dreaming,' murmured Tina. 'Take her up to the field and see if she still obeys you.'

All the way to the field Streaker was as good as gold, trotting quietly by my side. When we got there I let her off the lead. She went speeding off at once and I thought that was it, but as soon as I shouted 'Walkies!' Streaker came hurtling straight back again.

Tina couldn't stop laughing. 'That was what you said to her when you put her on the exercising machine – "Walkies!" For some reason it makes her come straight back to you. It's brilliant, Trev! Streaker's been trained!'

It took several seconds for this to sink in properly. Tina was right. Streaker *was* trained. That meant we hadn't lost the bet *and* she could come off Death Row! Everything was going to be all right. We stared at each other with enormous grins inside ourselves. I almost hugged Tina. (*Almost*, I said!)

Tina and I were still celebrating this when something even more unexpected happened. Streaker was charging round the woods, doing her normal everyday impression of a cruise missile, when we heard startled cries and Charlie Smugg suddenly appeared on the path. He wasn't alone. Sharon Blenkinsop was with him, and THEY WERE HOLDING HANDS!!!!!

They stared at us in horror. I wish you could have seen Charlie's face. He was furious, he was scared, he was worried, he was embarrassed, he wanted to die – and all at the same time. He hurriedly let go of Sharon's hand, but it was too late. We had seen everything.

'Hi, Charlie,' said Tina, ever-so-sweetly. 'Got yourself a girlfriend?'

'No, I haven't!' His face was getting very red.

'Charlie!' cried Sharon, punching his shoulder. 'You said!'

Tina and I had to bite our lips to stop ourselves from laughing out loud.

Charlie's eyes narrowed to dangerous slits. 'If you breathe a word to anyone, I'll kill you both,' he threatened. 'It was your pesky dog's fault. My dad says she should be put down. She's uncontrollable.'

Just at that moment Streaker went whizzing past. 'Walkies!' I shouted, and she came racing back, skidded on all fours and sat obediently by my side. 'She's no trouble,' I said. 'I've trained her.' Charlie's face turned white.

'I don't believe it,' he said hoarsely.

'You better had,' said Tina. 'We've won that bet, Charlie, and that means that you've lost, and THAT means that you've got to wash in the old tin bath.'

Oh no – there was no way Charlie was going to let this happen! He pulled himself up to his full height. He knew there was no way we could force him into that bath.

'Oh yeah?' he sneered. 'Who's going to make me? You two wimps? You've got to be joking!'

Charlie was right of course. We had no chance of getting him into that tub, unless he got in himself, and he wasn't going to do that in a million years.

'It was a bet,' said Tina. 'And you agreed to it.'

'Get lost!'

Tina folded her freckled arms across her chest and sighed. 'Well, I'm afraid that leaves us no choice. We shall just have to tell all your friends that we saw you in the woods holding hands with Sharon Blenkinsop.'

'Charlie!' squeaked Sharon, hands to her mouth in horror.

'You wouldn't!' spluttered Charlie.

'Of course we would. We had a bet,

Charlie, and we won. Either you get in that tin bath . . .'

'And don't forget to wash your hair,' I added.

'. . . or we tell your pals that you've got a girlfriend – lover-boy!' Charlie caved in. He was completely crestfallen. 'It's the last day of the holiday tomorrow,' Tina went on. 'You can have until then to decide. See you tomorrow, Charlie!'

Tina and I set off home. I shouted 'Walkies!' and Streaker came bursting out from the grass and trotted home with us, tail wagging cheerfully. (If I'd had a tail at that moment, mine would have been wagging like crazy!)

Dad had just got in and we showed him and Mum how obedient the dog was. They were pretty amazed of course, and why not? It *was* amazing! Mum handed over the thirty pounds and said it was worth every penny. I reminded her that I owed money for the dog-biscuits and her tights and the phone bill. She told me to forget it. The dog behaved herself and that was worth a fortune. Even Dad gave way eventually, but that was only because he had brought home a new golfing video (*Fifty Classic Golf Shots* – I ask you! Bring on those tanks!) and he wanted some peace and quiet so that he could sit down and watch it.

And that's it, really. It was great to have thirty pounds sitting in my pocket. The only thing I felt a little bad about was teasing Charlie over having a girlfriend. 'After all,' I said to Tina, 'we've never liked being teased about it.'

'We're different,' Tina explained. 'Charlie didn't want anybody to know about him and Sharon.'

'So?'

'We don't mind,' said Tina, giving me her ever-so-sweet smile. 'I like being your girlfriend and I don't care how many people know.'

I was thunderstruck. I suppose I should have seen it coming. I thought: No, no! Please, not this! Not after everything I've been through! Tina began to sort of lean towards me.

I think it was the first time I had ever moved faster than Streaker.

2010 is Puffin's **70th** anniversary year and you're invited to celebrate with us

8th May is

NATIONAL PUFFIN DAY

Share a Story with someone you love

If you want to join our year-long party go to **www.puffin.co.uk** for everything you need to know.

Includes information about brand new books, film screenings, exhibitions, merchandise and more. Just IMAGINE all the fun you can have . . .

There's a Puffin for everyone

'START NOT – NOR DEEM MY SPIRIT FLED;
IN ME BEHOLD THE ONLY SKULL,
FROM WHICH, UNLIKE A LIVING HEAD,
WHATEVER FLOWS IS NEVER DULL.'

LORD BYRON

THE
BOOK
OF
SKULLS

THE
BOOK
OF
SKULLS

Faye Dowling

Laurence King Publishing

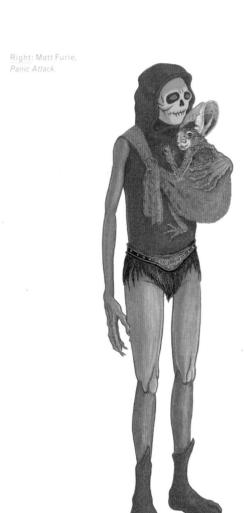

Left: Noel McLaughlin,
skulls at the Crypt
of the Sepulchral
Lamp at the Paris
catacombs, France.

THE CULT OF THE SKULL

Since its renaissance in the 1970s, the skull has emerged as one of the most recognizable symbols of today's contemporary visual landscape. Reborn through the music, fashion and art of an alternative youth culture, it has evolved from its spiritual and religious origins to become an icon for a post-modern society consumed by the desire to set itself apart from the crowd.

From African charms to Mayan sculptures, Greek myths to Aztec legends, Buddhist gods to Catholic martyrs, Shakespearian verse to Gothic stories, the skull appears throughout the myth and legend of human culture. A sacred symbol of luck or intellect, protection or fear, flesh or the soul, death or resurrection, divinity or the devil, its mystical and spiritual powers have captivated humanity and cast the skull as an emblem for the human consciousness, a memento mori through which to explore our fascination with the transience of life, death and the human soul.

Repurposed and recast by artists, illustrators and designers, this morbid motif has found its way into the visual vocabulary of urban life, a smiley face for a gothic generation, its macabre and mystic meanings re-appropriated by a disaffected youth as a timeless symbol of anarchy, rebellion and revolution. From the Misfits to Massive Attack, Andy Warhol to Alexander McQueen, Hello Kitty to The Mighty Boosh, Dalí to Damien Hirst, the skull has straddled the worlds of music, fashion, art and popular culture to become today's ultimate anti-establishment icon, a tribal emblem encapsulating the spirit of rock, punk, goth, skate and street cultures, and a universal shorthand for cool.

Bringing together artwork and images from across the fields of visual art and culture, *The Book of Skulls* pays tribute to the global phenomenon of the skull, the most revered icon of our times.

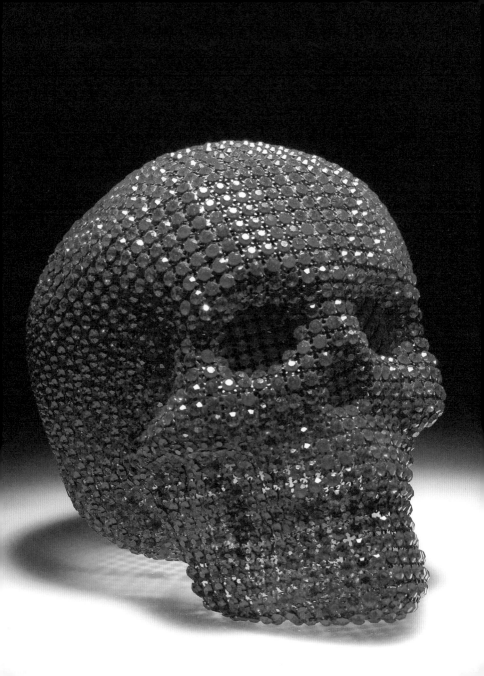

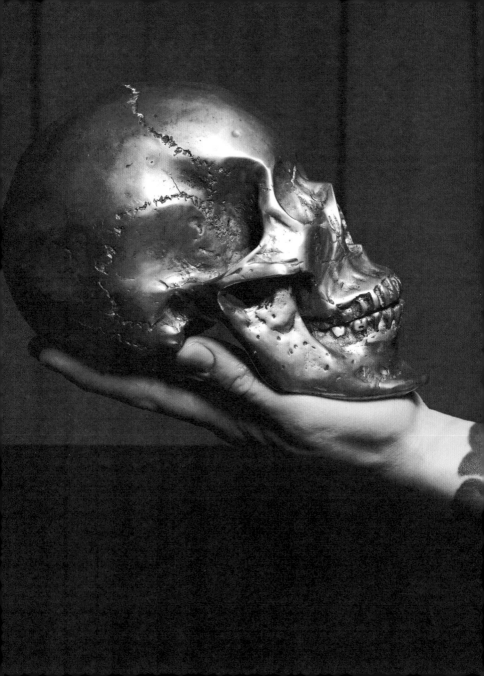

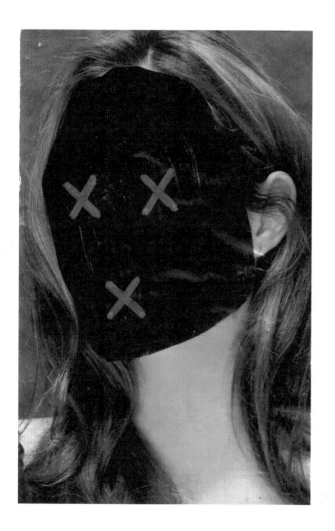

Previous spread:
Telegramme,
Prêt à Porter,
poster, metallic
silver screenprint
on Colourplan
paper. Telegramme's
decorative celtic
patterns create
a skull print for
a pop generation.

Left and right:
Chris Graham,
Look (Fuck) magazine.
Graham's pop
collages scrape
beneath the skin
of celebrity culture.

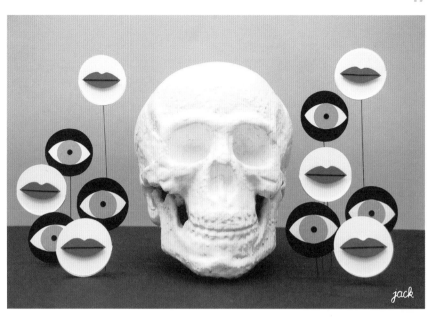

Page 16: Jasper Goodall, *Medusa*, from the 'Poster Girl' series.

Page 17: Julien Choquart & Camille Hirigoyen / JACK, stills from 'Miracle Man' music video for Cocosuma. JACK uses old-school animation in their pop–goth animated music video.

Left: Noah Scalin, *Skullphabet*, typeface design.

Right: Noah Scalin, *347. Skulledelic*. The success of Scalin's Skull-A-Day blog is testament to the draw of the skull as a contemporary pop icon. Since publishing his book *Skulls* in 2008, Scalin's designs have been widely used, here as a unique knitwear print by boutique brand Sibling.

Left: Donnachie
Simionato & Son with
Sergei Sviatchenko,
Throw the Dice,
poster artwork for
Acido Surtido.

Right: Bela Borsodi,
Triathlon, fashion
editorial. Borsodi's
graphic still lifes
transform accessories
into kitsch fashion
statements.

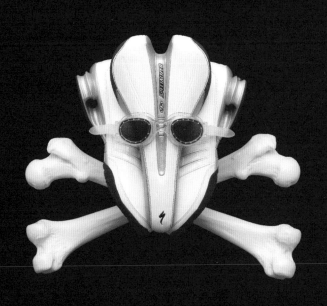

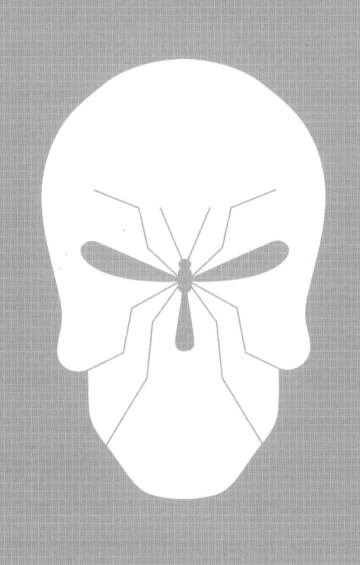

Left: Noma Bar,
Malaria, illustration
for *The Guardian*.

Right: James Hopkins,
Le Visage de Vanitas.

Page 24: Noma Bar,
Bloody Black (oil fights),
illustration for *FHM*
magazine. The skull
becomes a universal
metaphor in Bar's
graphic editorial
illustrations.

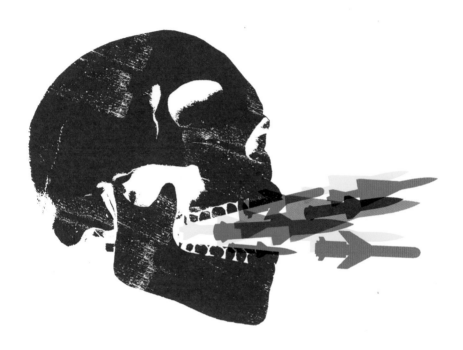

Page 25: Mirko Ilić
Terrorism and the Mafia,
sculpture for *Panorama*
magazine. Ilić enlists
the skull as a symbol
for death in his dark
visual sculpture.

Above: Patrick
Thomas, *The Atomic
Bazaar: The Rise
of the Nuclear Poor*,
screenprint for *The
New York Times Book
Review* cover.

Right: Noma Bar,
Red Tears, illustration,
personal project.

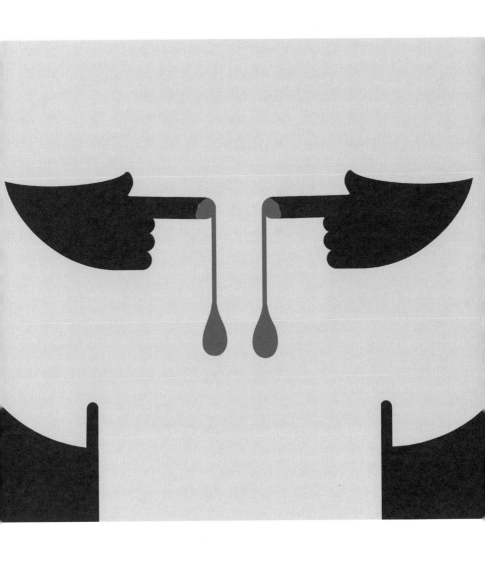

Right: Boo Davis /
Quiltsrÿche,
Skullfucked, quilt
design based on
Half-Log Cabin
pattern, cotton with
ink silkscreening.
Davis transforms
traditional quilt craft
with her graphic
skull motif.

Above: Boo Davis /
Quiltsrÿche,
Basketcase, quilt
design based
on Basket Weave
pattern, cotton.

Above and right: Ian
Wright, *(Mr.) Skull*,
1 inch badges.
Wright lends his iconic
illustration to the skull
in this glow-in-the-
dark creation.

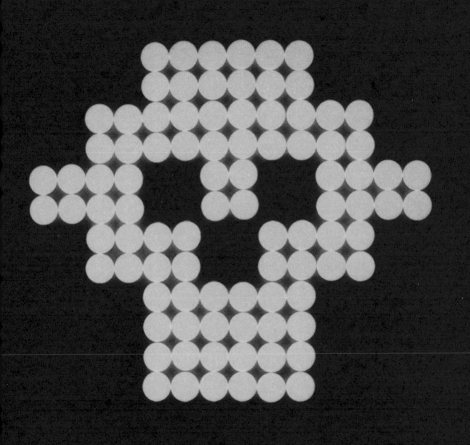

Left and right: Sergei Sviatchenko, *Art for Art's Sake*, collages from original pictures by Walter Bettens and Siegrid Demyttenaere. Commissioned by *DAMn Magazine* in conjunction with the 52nd edition of the Venice Art Biennale and Documenta 12. Sviatchenko catches the spirit of Venice's art culture in his homage to artworks such as Subodh Gupta's *Very Hungry God* sculpture.

Above:
MEGAMUNDEN, *Sugar Skull*, illustration.

Right: Shepard Fairey, *Dia de los Muertos*. Fairey lends his famous graphic style to the Mexican Day of the Dead.

Left: José Guadalupe Posada, *La Calavera Catrina*, 1913. Posada's 'The Elegant Skull' has become a mascot of the Day of the Dead celebrations.

Right: Mixquic town cemetery, Day of the Dead, Mexico, 1963.

LA SANTA MUERTE

The Mexican Day of the Dead can be traced back thousands of years through the rituals and beliefs of Mayan, Mixtec and Aztec civilizations. Defined by its vibrant displays of flowers, food and skulls made of sugar, the festival is entwined in the history of Mexican art and culture and remains one of the most significant celebrations of death in modern society. The festival has its roots in the ancient myth of the goddess Mictecacihuatl, the Lady of the Dead, who ruled over the underworld of Mictlan. Wearing the mask of a skull, she escorted the newly departed back to their departed families and kept watch over the bones of the dead. On the 1st and 2nd of November families decorate the graves of their loved ones with drawings called 'calaveras' (skulls) to evoke the spirits of the dead to hear the prayers and thoughts of the living.

Above: Richard
Fairhead, *The General
(Hungry for Unrest)*,
personal project.

Right: Wes
Lang, *The Risk
of Being Ignored*.

LIFE HERE IS GRAND...

Left: Wes Lang,
Genesis Part 2 (Death).
Lang explores life and
death in his textural
drawings and murals.

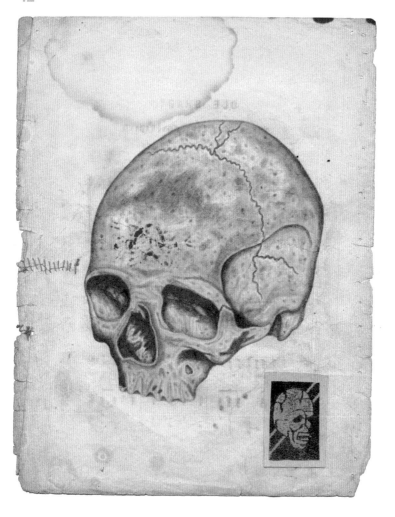

Above: Wes Lang,
*The Legend of Ole
Shady*, pencil on paper.

Right: Bert Industries,
*The Evil Children's
Flower Shop*, 2008,
pen and watercolour.

The strangest flower shop I ever did see   Dr Best

★LOS PISTOLOS★

MODERN LIFE IS RUBBISH!

The rubbishmen of Soho London say: IN THE AGE OF BRITANNIA POP A BEAT COMBO OF MOCKNEY BOYS DID DECLARE "MODERN LIFE IS RUBBISH" AND WE DO AGREE SOMEWHAT. TIS TIME TO TAKETH TO THEE STREETS AND TO BURN OUR YFRONTS AND DANCE AND DRINK AND SCREW. AND TO PUKE ON PARLIAMENT AND SUCH STUFF. HERE US NOW THE @naRCHISTIC ACIDIC PEOPLES BRASS BANDF THE REPUBLIC OF SOHO ARE MARCHING THE PROLETARIAT MUST TURN OFF THE TV, AND ERECT A GIANT DAYGLOW MAYPOLE IN PARLIAMENT SQUARE AND DO A MERRY DANCE OF DEFIANCE AND SHOUT DOWN WITH DETRITUS MAYDAY

PETER GETS HIGH
A MAN CALLED PETER CLIMBED A LADDER TODAY AND ENJOYED A NICE VIEW

TV MASSAGE €25 IN SOHO PUB

Schädelfıck COMING SOON

K.UNST

! KOOL KIDS
ON PLANT FERTILIZER SAY NAY TO KETAMINE

LOVE eggs **Baby B10**

LORRAINE KELLY SAYS FREE YOUR MIND AND YOUR ASS WILL FOLLOW

SALES UP

WET FISH **Y B A TO VOTE TORY**

MIND YOUR HEAD

I AM GAY SAYS POPE

TOO MUCH DOG SHIT IN LONDON

DRINK MORE GIN

THE ICE AGE IS COMING

Pope was seen at the Joiners Amrs having bum fun !!!

VOID

ABU HAMZA TO REPLACE HARRY HILL ON TV BURP
LICK MY SPACE SHIP

BEWARE OF € PERIOD AHEAD TAKE YOUR MONEY OUT OF THE BANKS AND RUN TO THE HILLS

PEOPLE OF DALSTON RIP DAVID CAMRONS FACE OFF !!!
WHEN DAVES FACE WAS ON A BILLBOARD IN DALSTON THE GOOD PEOPLE OF DALSTON TOOK UMBRAGE AND RIPPED IT OFF.

SUBCOMANDANTE MARCOS ROCKS

MAYDAY MELT DOWN
THE FOUR HORSEMEN OF APOCALYPSE AND THE WOMBLES AND THE GREAT UNWASHED AMASS ON PARLIAMENT SQUARE. 1.5.10 PM

OPIUM FOR THE PEOPLE
NHS TO GIVE FREE OPIUM TO ALL BRITISH CITIZENS MAN LETS OFF ON BUS !

WE ARE The writing ON the WALL @

CURVY CLAIRE RETIRES !
AFTER SEVEN YEARS OF ESCORTING

CELEBRITY DIET
WILL GIVE YOU BARE BONES IN A WEEK

NICK GRIFFIN TO BE JUDGE ON X FACTOR
THE END IS NOW

WAR STILL ON IN IRAQ
WAR STILL ON IN AFGHANISTAN !

TRAMP JUICE
IS GOOD FOR YOU STREET DRINKERS OF THE WORLD DECLARE

STRANGE BREW

HERE AND NOW

FOR MORE STUFF GO TO WWW.ROBERTRUBBISH.BLOGSPOT.COM

Left: Robert Rubbish,
Los Pistolos. Rubbish
echoes early folk
etchings with his
contemporary
comic 'calaveras'.

Above: Robert
Rubbish, *The Man
Who Taught His
Ass To Talk*.

Left and above: Neal
Fox, details from *2000
Light Years from Home*.
Fox tells modern
macabre tales in
his black-and-white
illustrations.

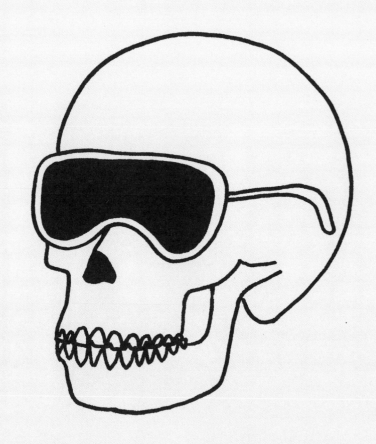

DEAD COOL

Left: James Joyce,
Dead Cool, gicleé
print, edition of ten.

Above: Drew
Millward, *Try Smiling*,
cover artwork
for Citizens' 2009
debut EP.

Below: Savage
Pencil, *Really Grimm*.
Pencil's ink drawings
have won him iconic
status as a cult
comic illustrator.

Right: Savage Pencil,
Curse of Mad.

Far right: Savage
Pencil, *Scalp Hell*.

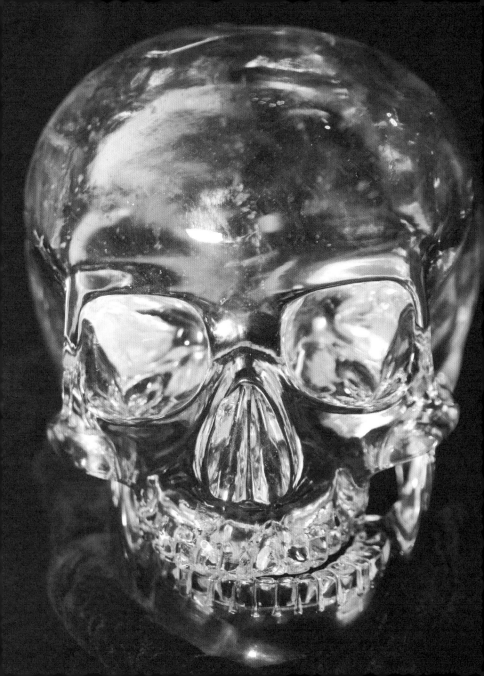

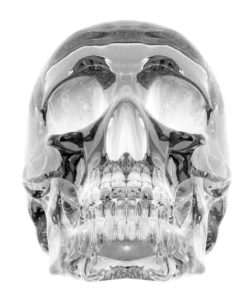

Left: *The Skull of Doom*, the infamous Mitchell-Hedges crystal skull, discovered in 1924.

Right: Shiva, *Crystal Skull*, illustration.

THE CRYSTAL SKULL

The crystal skull was an object of great intrigue in late Victorian society. Imported from Mexico by pioneering antiquarians such as Eugéne Boban, the skulls were toted as relics of ancient Aztec or Mayan civilizations and their popularity gave rise to a vigorous trade in fake pre-Columbian artefacts throughout the late 19th century. The infamous Mitchell-Hedges skull was discovered in 1924 by Anna Le Guillon Mitchell-Hedges, adopted daughter of the British adventurer and popular author F.A. Mitchell-Hedges, and was reportedly used by the High Priest of Maya as a charm to will death, a legend coining its nickname *The Skull of Doom*. Mitchell-Hedges also claimed that the skull caused visions and held paranormal mystical powers, a line adopted by fantasy and science fiction writers of the 1960s and 70s, through whom the crystal skull re-emerged in New Age mythology as a relic of ancient Atlantis. No catalogued research has ever proved the authenticity of the crystal skulls, but our intrigue persists and they remain a cult collector's item to this day.

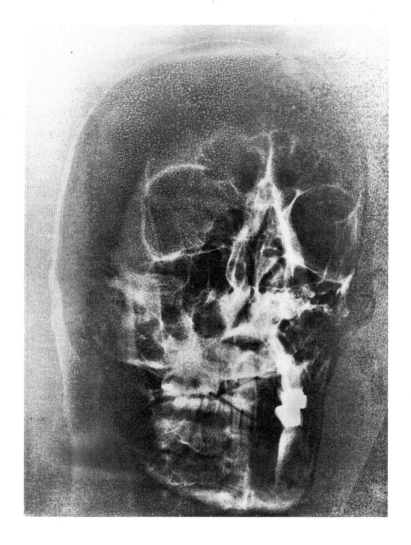

Above: Marc Atkins,
*The Hypaethral 22
(part iv)*. Atkins' print
explores the skull
as the threshold for
the human soul.

Right: James Aldridge,
Destroying Angel,
acrylic on canvas.

Above: Andres
Guerrero, illustration.

Right: Jesse Auersalo,
Knock On Wood,
cover illustration
for *Beautiful/Decay*
magazine. Auersalo
uses pop–goth tones
in his contemporary
fashion illustrations.

Left: Miss Bugs, *Hirst All Over My Body*, silkscreen and stencil on wood.

Right: Notter + Vigne, poster for 'An exhibition of unspeakable things – works inspired by H.P. Lovecraft's Commonplace Book' at the Maison d'Ailleurs, Switzerland.

L'EXPO QUI REND FOU
H. P. LOVECRAFT
ET LE LIVRE DE RAISON
AN EXHIBITION OF UNSPEAKABLE THINGS
WORKS INSPIRED BY H. P. LOVECRAFT'S COMMONPLACE BOOK

Maison d'Ailleurs, 28 octobre 07– 6 avril 08
Musée de la science-fiction, de l'utopie et des voyages extraordinaires
Place Pestalozzi 14 · Yverdon-les-Bains, Suisse · Tél. +41 24 425 64 38 · www.ailleurs.ch
Heures d'ouverture: mercredi, jeudi, vendredi: 14h-18h, samedi, dimanche: 12h-18h

ILFORD L'Hebdo ESPACE2 PAYOT

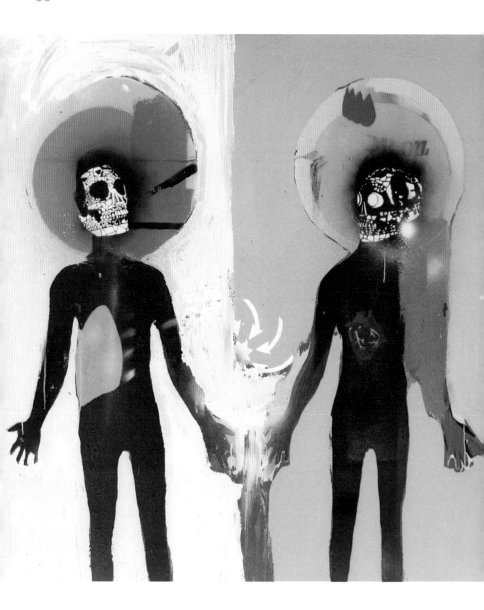

60

Left: Robert Del Naja
and Tom Hingston,
cover artwork for
'Splitting the Atom'
by Massive Attack.
Design by Tom
Hingston Studio. Art
by Robert Del Naja.

Above: Universal
Everything, video
still from MTV ident,
created by MTV
WDS Milan and Matt
Pyke of Universal
Everything.

Left and inset: Sergei
Sviatchenko, *Art for
Art's Sake*, collages
from original pictures
by Walter Bettens and
Siegrid Demyttenaere.
Commissioned by
DAMn Magazine (see
also page 32). Here,
the artist pays homage
to artists such as
Subodh Gupta (left)
and El Anatsui (inset).

Page 64: Mathis
Rekowski, illustration.

Page 65: Carl Burgess,
Human Remains.

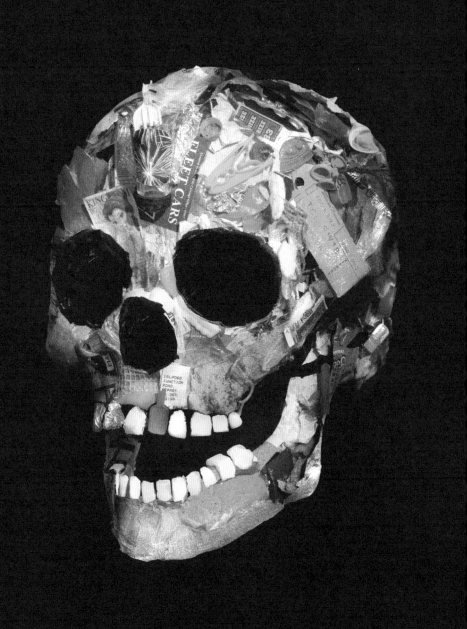

Left: Kid Zoom,
installation, wrecked
car, stickers, aerosol.
Kid Zoom celebrates
the skull as urban
street icon.

Above: Kid Zoom,
installation, aerosol
on car and house,
Perth, Australia.

Left: Street artist Chaz
Bojorquez, *LA Madusa*,
1997, acrylic on paper.

Right: Chaz Bojorquez
as Señor Suerte,
1974, Los Angeles.
Photographed by
Blades Bojorquez.
Bojorquez's Señor
Suerte skull tags
have become icons
of Mexican–Amercian
street art.

SEÑOR SUERTE

In the late 1960s young Mexican–American art student Chaz Bojorquez
began painting on the underground sewage tunnels of West Los
Angeles. Inspired by the territorial 'cholo' graffiti of Chicano
neighbourhood gangs, Bojorquez experimented with typographical
symbols and signs in what was to become one of the first examples
of stencilled art applied to the streets. In 1969 he created 'Señor Suerte'
(Mr Luck), a stylized skull tag with crossed fingers and a sardonic smile
which was adopted by local gangs as a sign of protection against death
on the tough streets of Los Angeles. Bojorquez's art has influenced
generations of graffiti artists and the skull remains a key icon in
contemporary street art with artists such as Michael Leon and KAWS
keeping the skull synonymous with the spirit of the streets.

Above: *Skullphone*
× *FAILE*, Shoreditch,
London, photograph
by Shane R.J. Walter.
Walter's work has
captured the skull
as an urban art icon
around the globe.

Right: Pure Evil,
Pure Evel Knievel,
Shoreditch, London,
photograph by
Shane R.J. Walter.

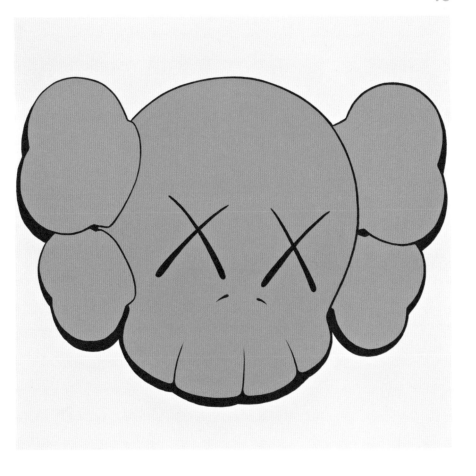

Above: KAWS,
Untitled, acrylic
on canvas. KAWS'
collaborations with
brands such as
Stussy and KidRobot
have made his skull
face logo an icon of
contemporary street
art and culture.

Left: *Sakuragicho*,
Graffiti Mile,
Yokohama, photograph
by Shane R.J. Walter.

Page 74: KAWS,
Chum (White), 2009,
painted bronze,
47 × 33 × 15.2cm
(20½ × 13 × 6 inches),
edition of 3.

Page 75: KAWS,
Chum (Black), 2009,
painted bronze,
47 × 33 × 15.2cm
(20½ × 13 × 6 inches),
edition of 3.

Left: Chaz Bojorquez,
Los Avenues, 1987,
serigraph, edition
of 40, 6 colours plus
3 spray can stencils.

Right: Unknown
street artists, Hoxton,
London, 2001,
photograph by Shane
R.J. Walter.

Below: *Sweet Toof
× Cyclops*, Brick
Lane, London, 2007,
photograph by Shane
R.J. Walter.

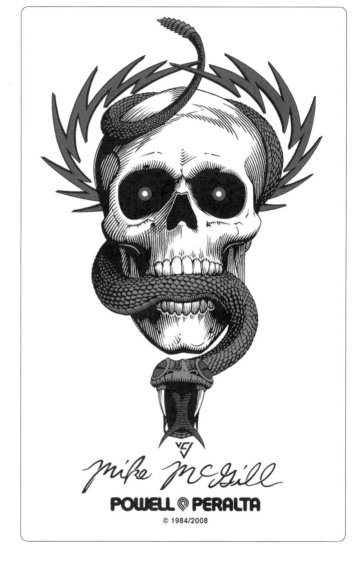

Right: Vernon
Courtland Johnson
aka VCJ, Mike Mills
skull card design for
Powell Peralta. Powell
Rats skateboarding
typified the 1970's
skate culture, their
skull logo and designs
setting the stage for
skate culture's alliance
with the skull.

Far Right: Chaz
Bojorquez, *R.I.P Sk8*,
Insta, acrylic paint
on canvas.

Above: Skull Skates,
logo. LA-based Skull
Skates works with
artists such as Michael
Leon to create their
iconic skateboards
and accessories.

Right: Mike Ballard,
The All Of Everything,
installation. Ballard's
piece takes his
gothic imagery to
three-dimensional
proportions.

Above: Mike Giant, *Aisha* (left) and *Krissy* (right). LA-based artist Mike Giant encapsulates the culture of the skull in his posters, artworks, photography and tattoo art.

Right: Mike Giant, *Fallen Angel*.

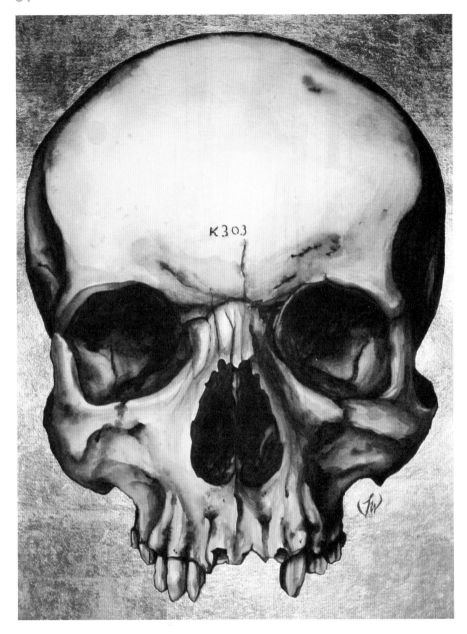

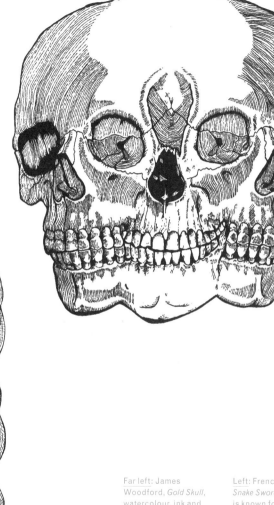

Far left: James Woodford, *Gold Skull*, watercolour, ink and gold leaf on paper. Woodford draws on the celtic and military history of the skull in his gothic paintings and tattoos.

Left: French, *Skull Snake Sword*. French is known for his dark, morbid illustrations exploring death and the dark side of life.

Above: French, *3 × The Radness*.

Left: James
Woodford, *Rest in
Pieces*, watercolour
ink and gold leaf
on paper.

Right: Stix and
Jones, *Vanitas*, oil on
skateboards. Stix and
Jones envisage gothic
skull designs for
murals, skateboards
and motorcycles.

Above: Stephanie
Henderson, *Non Omnis
Moriar*, oil on canvas.

Right: Scott Move,
Holding On, black
ink on A4 paper.

Left: Rik Rawling,
*The Hangman's
Breakfast*, acrylic
and ink on card.

Right: Scott Move,
Burning Baby, black
ink on A4 paper.

Left: Hell's Angels,
New York, 1979.

Right: *Hells Angels on
Wheels*, film still, 1967.
This cult film starred
Jack Nicholson and
Adam Roarke.

FOREVER ANGELS

Tattoos, long hair, leather and steel. As epitomized in Dennis Hopper's
Easy Rider in 1969, the biker lifestyle has become synonymous with the
societal landscape of the 1960s. The Hells Angel Motorcycle Club was
a counter-culture society formed in Fontana, California, in 1948 and
today has over 100 chapters all over the world. Their 'Death's Head'
skull insignia was designed by Frank Sadilek, past president of the San
Francisco chapter, and was based on the insignias of the First World
War 85th Fighter Squadron and the 552nd Medium Bomber Squadrons.
Beyond the biker jackets and rallies, a darker side of reported violence,
drug dealing and trafficking led the Federal Bureau of Investigation
to class the Angels as one of the most dangerous gangs in the United
States of America. Their motto, 'When we do right, nobody remembers.
When we do wrong, nobody forgets.'

Previous spread:
MEGAMUNDEN, *Sugar
Skull* (see page 34),
tattoo inked by Lucy
at Into You, London.

Above: Craig Robson,
Swords and Scrolls.

Right: Craig
Robson, *Depths*.

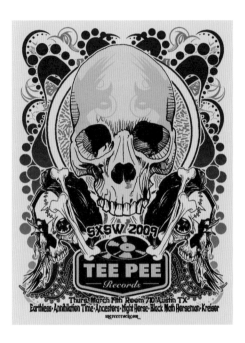

Above left: Brian
Mercer, *Tee Pee
Records Showcase*,
silkscreened poster
design. Mercer's
screenprints use
a modern take
on the classic era
of rock illustration.

Above right: Brian
Mercer, *Year Long
Disaster*, silkscreened
poster design.

Right: Brian
Mercer, *Lord by Fire/
Deadbird/Hail!Hornet*,
silkscreened
poster design.

Page 102: Vincent
Castiglia, *Gnosis*,
sculpture.

Page 103: Shepard
Fairey, *Obey Misfits
Fiend Skull*, screenprint.
Fairey redraws the
famous Misfits logo
(see page 109) for
a new punk generation.

Left: Mike Giant, *Skate
Virgin*, limited edition
poster design.

Above: Mike Giant,
Black Altar, illustration.

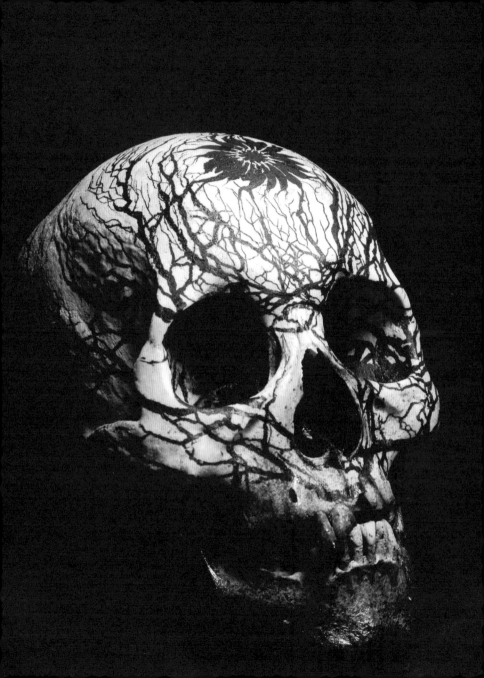

Left: William Gedney, photograph of Ron 'Pigpen' McKernan, Grateful Dead concert, California, 1968.

Right: Album artwork for 'Steal Your Face' by Grateful Dead, 1976, lettering by Rick Griffin. The Grateful Dead's famous 'stealie' skull logo was designed by Robert D Thomas and was the first appearance of the skull as rock music icon.

Page 106: Stanley Mouse and Alton Kelley, *Skeleton and Roses*, poster artwork for the Grateful Dead, 1966.

Page 107: Mouse and Kelley, album artwork for 'Memorial', 1970.

THE DEAD HEADS

The American rock band the Grateful Dead encapsulated the spirit of hippy culture with their eclectic music and legendary live performances. Through the work of Stanley Mouse and Alton Kelley, the band's artwork has come to define the visual language of the 1960s. Mouse and Kelley combined celtic lettering and symbols with psychedelic illustrations, reviving traditional skull motifs such as the crown of roses, a celtic symbol for 'carpe diem', in posters and artwork which encapsulated the freewheeling spirit of the times. As the new wave of rock culture emerged throughout the 1970s the skull reappeared as the anarchic emblem of punk pioneers the Misfits and has since come to define rock, punk and heavy metal culture as the ultimate symbol of rebellion.

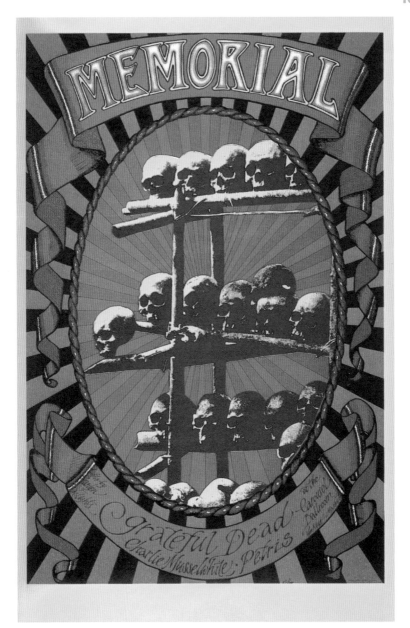

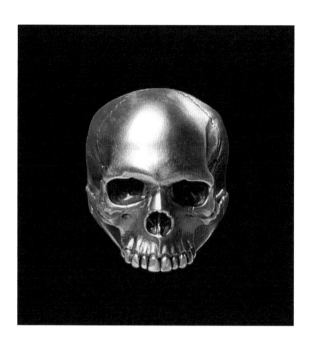

Page 108: Ben
Brown, *Kiss*, brush
and ink, t-shirt print
for Supply.

Page 109: Misfits,
Fiend Skull logo.
Created in 1979
for their 'Horror
Business' single,
the Misfits' skull
logo has become
an icon of
contemporary
rock culture.

Above: Courts and
Hackett, *Skull Ring*.
Originally designed
in 1978, Courts and
Hackett silver skull
ring was given as
a gift to the The
Rolling Stones'
Keith Richards and
has since become
a coveted rock icon.

Far left: Courts and
Hackett, *Skull Ring*.
18ct yellow and white
gold ring. Pave set
with diamonds. The
intricate diamond ring
is side engraved with
a Grim Reaper scythe,
tumbling dice and
falling playing cards.

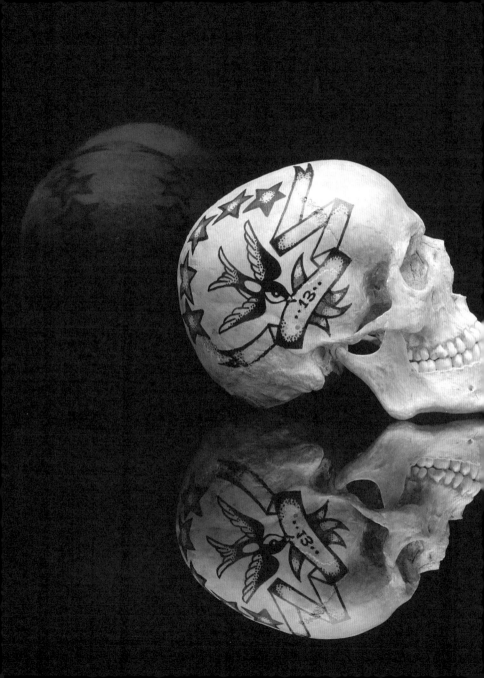

Far left: Stephen Thompson, *Persona Non Grata*, embroidery for jackets, printed t-shirts and scarves for John Richmond boutique, Paris.

Left: Alexander McQueen, skull ring. McQueen's dark, romantic designs made the aesthetics of goth culture synonymous with contemporary style and transformed the skull into a modern fashion icon.

Above: Alexander McQueen, skull clutch bag.

Right: Andrei
Molodkin, study
for the installation
'Oil Evolution',
mixed technique.

Inset: Andrei
Molodkin, *Sweet
Crude Eternity*, crude
oil in the form of
Madonna and skull.

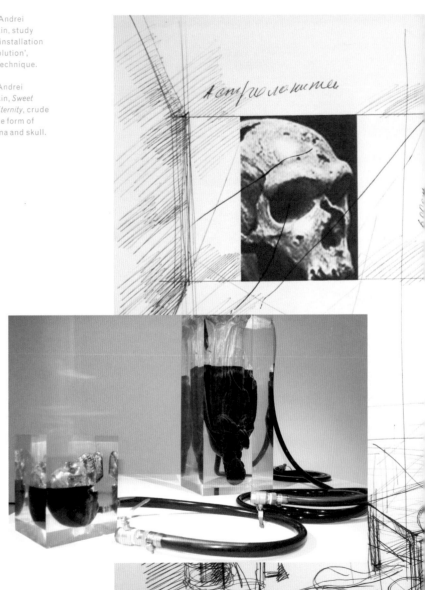

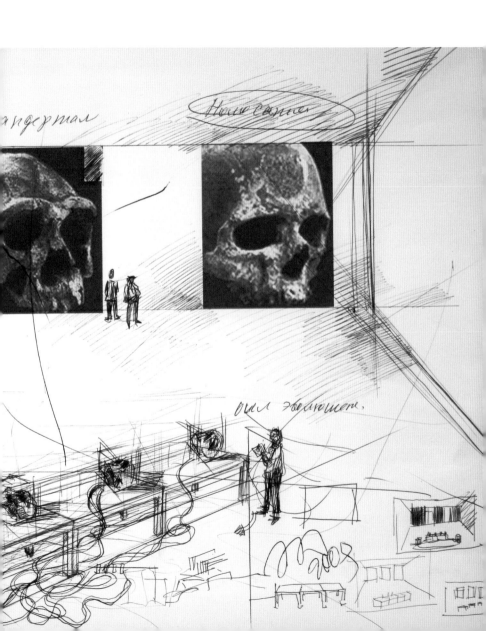

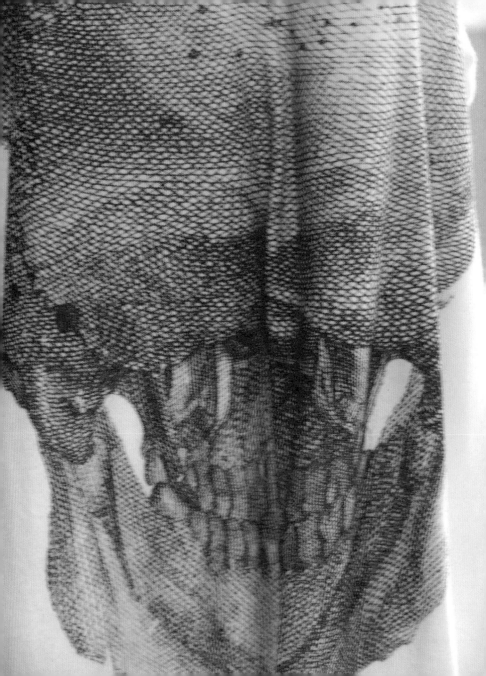

Left: Alexander
McQueen, skull
print scarf, 2002.
McQueen's iconic
scarf was first created
for his Spring / Summer
2003 collection and
remains one of the
late designer's best
selling items.

Previous spread:
Atlanta Rascher,
fashion still life
for *Arena Homme+*
magazine. Art
direction and set
design by Patrick
Waugh. Rascher's
fashion editorial
celebrates the skull
in contemporary
fashion and
accessories design.

Above: Phoebe
Richardson,
skull dinner plate.
Richardson's skull
series demonstrates
the allure of the skull
as a luxury icon.

Left: Danielle Levitt, *Shiloh*, photograph for *Dazed & Confused* magazine, 2010. Levitt's series portrays the gothic teenagers of the Crimson Wolf Pack in Southern Texas, a subculture which demonstrates the ongoing allure of the morbid in contemporary youth culture.

Right: Danielle Levitt, *Wofie Blackheart*, photograph for *Dazed & Confused* magazine, 2010.

THE DARKNESS

Through the visions of fashion icons such as Alexander McQueen, Rick Owens and Gareth Pugh, the mood and aesthetics of goth culture have become central to the fashion culture of the 21st century. Born in the post-punk era of the 1980s, the goth aesthetic drew from the new Romanticism of 19th century gothic literature, embracing notions of horror, alienation and the morbid as an ideological framework for life – and it survives today as one of the longest standing subcultures of the 20th century. Engrained in the music, fashion and youth culture of the late 80s and 90s, goth culture's morbid aesthetics have been adopted by a new generation at one with the darker side of life.

Above and left:
Thomas Wylde,
kaftan and t-shirt
design, photographs
by Steven Duncan.

Right: Emilie
Morris, skull
necklace design.

Next spread, left
to right: Sandrine
Pelletier, *Engel 3
(Cupidon)*, *Snake*
and *Hydra*, pieces
made using lace,
latex and resin.

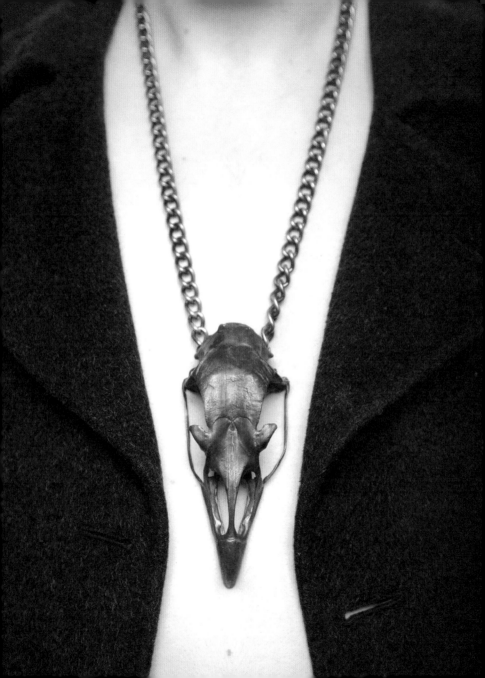

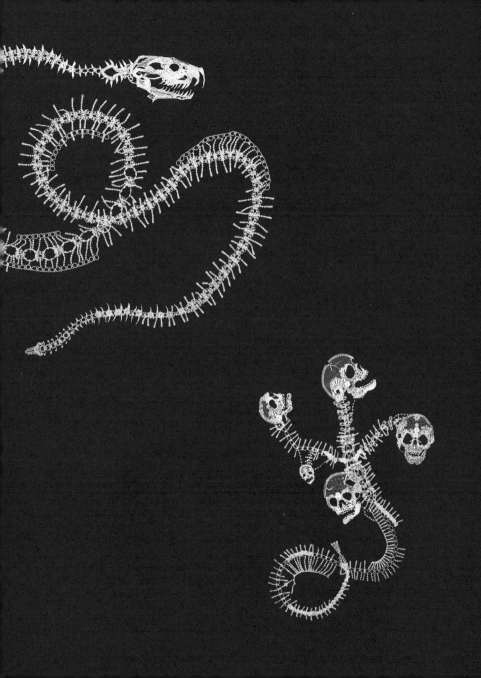

This spread: Vivienne Westwood, skull jewellery designs. Westwood brings gothic glamour to the skull with her punk fashion ideology.

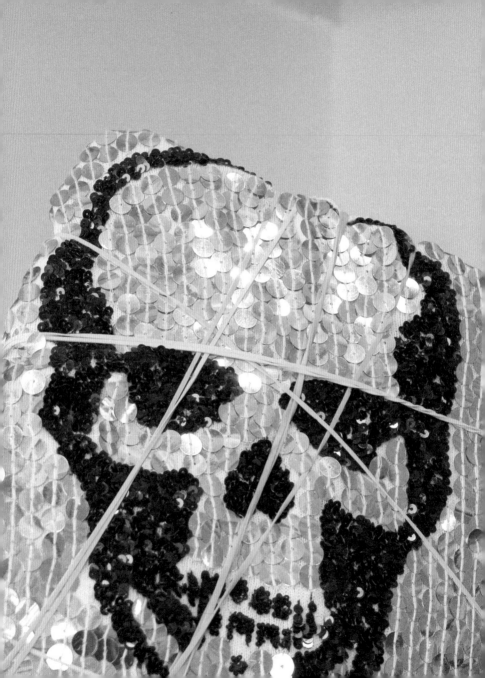

Left: Atlanta Rascher, fashion still life for *Arena Homme+* magazine. Art direction and set design by Patrick Waugh.

Below: Bert Industries, *Pygmy Skulls in Bell Jars*, 2008, carved bone, human hair and gilded spikes. Bert uses the skull as artistic statement in her dark explorations in drawing and sculpture.

Page 134: Nicola Bolla, *Vanitas 2006*, Swarovski crystals.

Page 135: Warren du Preez and Nick Thornton Jones, photograph of Alice Temple, 2007. Temple's unfinished skull tattoo was captured by the experimental image-makers for Unkle's 'War Stories' album.

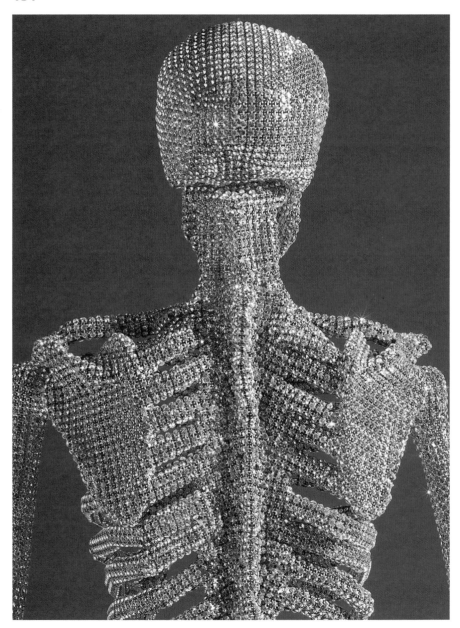

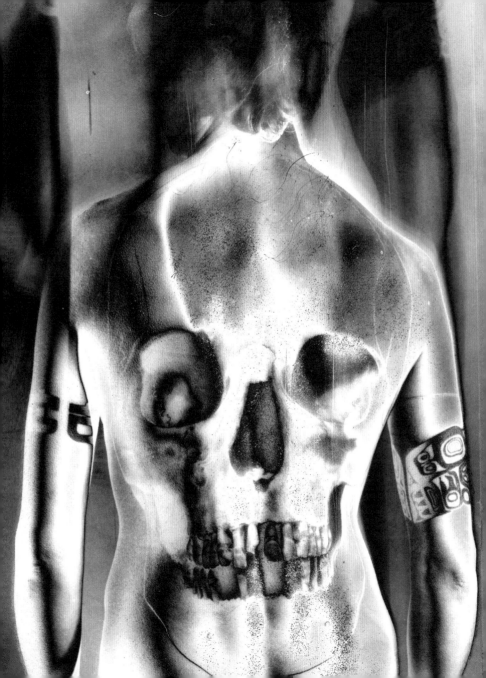

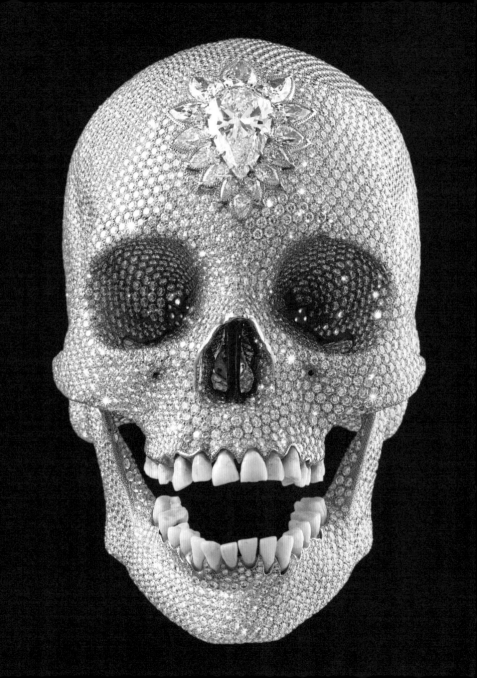

Left: Damien Hirst, *For the Love of God*, 2007. Platinum, diamonds and human teeth. Hirst's platinum cast of a human skull is covered with 8,601 diamonds and is estimated to be worth over £50 million.

Right: Damien Lhomme, *Vanité*, 1641. Lhomme's artwork typifies the vanitas paintings of the Renaissance period.

VANITAS

In the early 14th century the Black Death cast a grave shadow upon early Renaissance society, reminding people that Death, the 'great leveller', watched over them all. The Dance of Death emerged as a morbid satirical warning of the inevitability of death, and was visualized by artists such as Michael Wolgemut and later Hans Holbein. Over the decades emerged the 'vanitas', a type of still life painting depicting objects such as skulls, fruit and musical instruments presented as visual allegories for death and the transience of earthly things. Through this, the skull came to symbolize not only death, but greed and superficiality – a moral metaphor for vanity as the curse of modern life. Reinterpreted through the visions of contemporary artists from Dalí to Damien Hirst, the skull has survived decades of cultural and creative revolution as the ultimate symbol of life, death and human experience.

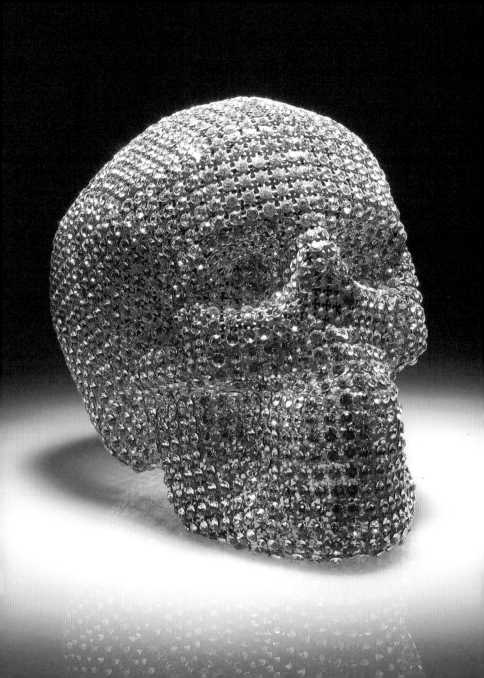

Previous spread:
Jan Van Oost,
Salomé, cast silver.

Left: Nicola Bolla,
Vanitas (White Skull),
2006, Swarovski
white crystals.
Bolla explores the
contemporary vanitas
in his beautiful crystal
skull series.

Below: Alastair
Mackie, *Cool Hand*,
from 'The Seven
Sleepers', mother
of pearl, black marble,
jasper, human skull.

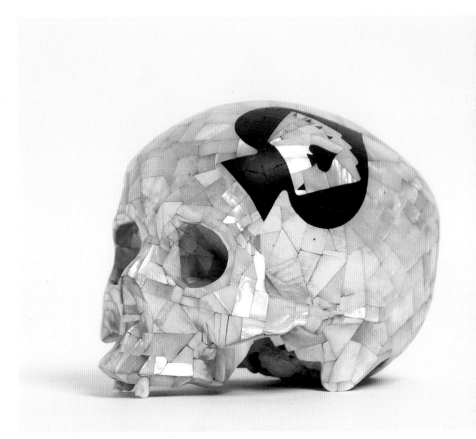

Left: Paul Insect,
Miss July, 2008, cast
bronze, stainless steel,
cocobolo, enamel
paint and mika flakes,
edition of 1.

Below: Wolfe von
Lenkiewicz, *Ace
of Spaces*, from the
'Plura Culture' series,
gouache and charcoal
on canvas with fixed
UV protection.

144

Left: Paul Insect, *Miss January*, 2008, cast bronze, stainless stell, cocobola, enamel paint, mika flakes, edition of 1.

Right: Bertozzi and Casoni, *Ossobello (Beautiful Bones)*, 2010, polychrome ceramic.

Above: Robert
Lazzarini, *Skull (iii)*,
resin, bone, pigment.

Right: Brian Dettmer,
Skull 11, 2007, altered
cassette tapes.

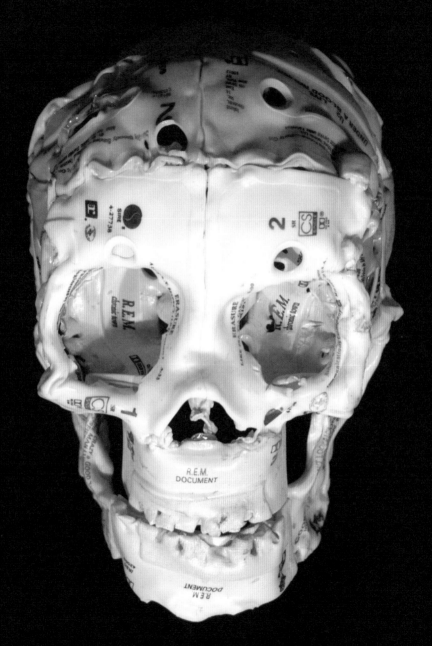

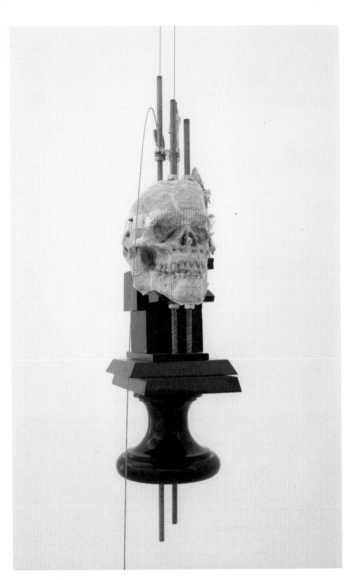

Above: Andrew
Zuckerman,
*Unidentified Gazelle
Skull*, Qatar.

Right: Tony Matelli,
Sad Skulls.

Left, above and next
spread: Alan Kane,
*Vanitas Vanitatum
Omnia Vanitas* :),
C-type photographs.
75 x 90 cm (30 x 35 in).
Kane's photographs
recontextualize classic
found patches from
.skull culture. Drawing
on biker culture
and DIY fashion,
his series presents
skull iconography
as an artistic and
anthropological motif
of popular culture.

Above: Amy Sarkisian,
*Encrusted Skull
(Ruby, Gold, Black).*
Sarkisian's skulls
are embellished
with beads, pearls
and sequins to
create decadent
gothic ornaments.

Right, bottom: Amy
Sarkisian, *Encrusted
Skull (Pearl with
White Teeth).*

Right, top: Amy
Sarkisian, *Encrusted
Skull (Red).*

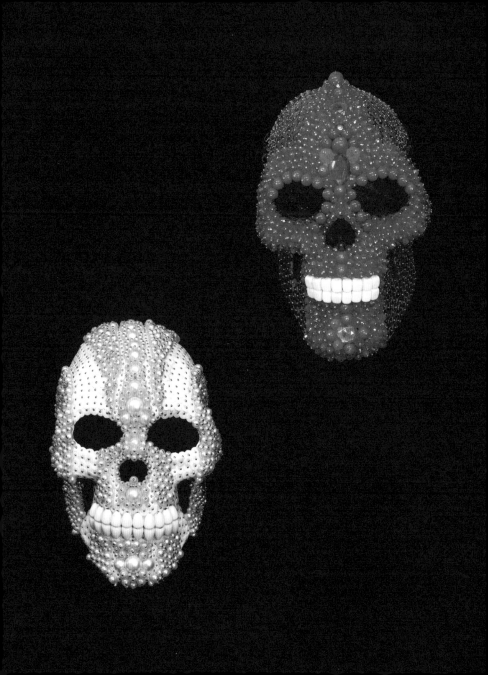

CREDITS

The publisher and author would like to thank the following artists, institutions and photographers for the use of their material. Every effort has been made to contact the copyright holder. In the event of any omissions please contact the publisher who will correct any mistakes for future editions:

9   Photograph courtesy Alfredini Sergio
10–11   Courtesy Gallery Almine Rech
23   Courtesy Max Wigram Gallery, London
30–31   Photograph by Asger Carlsen
36   © University of Michigan Museum of Art
37   © Jam Media / Getty Images
39–42   All images courtesy of the artist and V1 Gallery, Copenhagen
46–47   Courtesy Galerie Suzanne Tarasieve, Paris
52   Guillem Lopez / Alamy images
53   Shiva / Shutterstock
61   Creative direction by MTV WDS Milan and Matt Pyke / Universal Everything, directed by Matt Pyke / Universal Everything and Tronic, audio: Simon Pyke / Freefarm
69   Image from 'The Art and Life of Chaz Bojorquez', curated by Marco Klefisch and Alberto Scabbia, published by Damiani Editore, 2009
73–75   Courtesy of the artist and Honor Fraser Gallery, Los Angeles. Photograph by Josh White
76   Courtesy Chaz Bojorquez
92   © Keith Torrie / NY Daily News Archive / Getty Images
93   © Moviestore Collection Ltd / Alamy
103   Trademark and © Cyclopian Music Inc. All Rights Reserved. Reprinted with permission. www.Misfits.com
104   © The Gedney Collection, Duke University Archives
105–107   Courtesy Rhino Entertainment Company and Public Image © Warner Music Group Company
109   Trademark and © Cyclopian Music Inc. All Rights Reserved. Reprinted with permission. www.Misfits.com

110–111   David Courts and Bill Hackett. Post-production by Hammer Labs
122   Photograph by Nerys Jones
127   Photograph by Tom Kavanagh
130–131   Courtesy Vivienne Westood www.viviennewestwood.com
133   Photograph by Nerys Jones
134   Photograph courtesy Alfredini Sergio
136   Courtesy Science Ltd and Jay Jopling / White Cube, London. Photo by Prudence Cuming Associates Ltd via Getty Images
137   Courtesy Art Archive
140   Photograph courtesy Alfredini Sergio
141   Photograph by Francis Ware, courtesy of the David Roberts Collection
142   © Paul Insect
143   Courtesy All Visual Arts, London
144   © Paul Insect
145   Courtesy All Visual Arts, London. Photo by Tessa Angus
146   Image courtesy of the artist and Honor Fraser Gallery, Los Angeles
148   Courtesy Michael Stevenson gallery, Cape Town. Photograph by Mario Todeschini
149   Photography by Christophe Lebedensky
151   © Tony Matelli. Courtesy the artist and Cheim & Read, New York
152–155   Courtesy Ancient & Modern and the artist

Faye Dowling is a freelance editor, curator and art buyer specializing in photography, illustration, design, and contemporary visual culture. She has worked for magazines including *Dazed & Confused*, *Varoom*, *Frieze*, *Eye*, *Edit* and *Pictured*.

Right: Amy Sarkisian, *Encrusted Skull (Ruby Gold Black)*.

LAURENCE KING

Published in 2011 by
Laurence King Publishing Ltd
361–373 City Road
London EC1V 1LR
United Kingdom
Tel: + 44 20 7841 6900
Fax: + 44 20 7841 6910
email: enquiries@laurenceking.com
www.laurenceking.com

Reprinted 2011 (twice), 2012 (three times), 2013 (twice), 2014

A catalogue record for this book is available
from the British Library.

ISBN: 978 1 85669 700 2

Design by Praline

Printed in China

Cover: Telegramme, *Prêt à Porter*, poster.
Page 9: Nicola Bolla, *Vanitas*, Swarovski crystals.
Page 10–11: Hedi Slimane, *Skull* series, photograph
from Slimane's ongoing Diary project.

Lord Byron quotation from 'Lines Inscribed upon a Cup Formed From a Skull'.

MEMENTO
MORI